The Research and Development Engineer as Manager

▶▶▶▶▶▶▶▶▶▶▶▶▶▶▶▶▶▶▶

THOMAS MORANIAN
Rutgers · The State University

HOLT, RINEHART AND WINSTON
NEW YORK · CHICAGO · SAN FRANCISCO · TORONTO · LONDON

MODERN MANAGEMENT SERIES

G. Jay Anyon MANAGING AN INTEGRATED PURCHASING PROCESS

John Fayerweather FACTS AND FALLACIES OF INTERNATIONAL BUSINESS

Myron S. Heidingsfield and Frank H. Eby, Jr. MARKETING AND BUSINESS RESEARCH

Thomas Moranian THE R & D ENGINEER AS MANAGER

Edward B. Shils AUTOMATION AND INDUSTRIAL RELATIONS

Copyright © 1963 by Holt, Rinehart and Winston, Inc.
All rights reserved
Library of Congress Catalog Card Number: 63-13119
25819-0113
Printed in the United States of America

▶ ▶ ▶ ▶

Preface

For more than a decade I have been drawn to the fascinating challenge which R & D administration has presented to men of management and business education. Because of the uncertainties in the creative process, and particularly in R & D, many of the established decision-making processes and procedures applicable to other sectors of the firm — manufacturing, marketing, and finance — are of little value in the management of industrial research and development.

In the field of R & D administration much has been written and said about such topics as allocation of funds, project selection, organization, and working climate. Some of this material has insight; however, procedures do not yet exist to forecast and predict invention and discovery at a desirable level of reliability.

For some time a preponderance of study and investigation has been directed at top management's involvement with R & D administration and very little at the order of work and activity flowing from the engineer's bench. It seems to me that the first step should be an organized effort to gain understanding of what goes on at the project level, since the project, after all, is the object of top management's effort. Then from this understanding, managerial and administrative procedures can be developed to direct R & D operations effectively.

This study, therefore, is focused on the project work level and more specifically on the R & D engineer who is manager and leader of a project. Interest is centered sharply on the project leader in the context of his role in the budgetary process for the laboratory, which is inextricably associated with the engineering-economic factors operating at the project work level and all of which is of vital concern to the performance and progress of each R & D project engineer and scientist. For without proper management of the allocation of valuable laboratory resources, which must give weighted consideration to the scientific work at the laboratory bench and to conditions conducive to individual creativity, the output, progress, and development of the individual, and hence the total laboratory, are unquestionably impaired.

I believe this study is of significant value to engineers, scientists, and staff personnel responsible for industrial research and development work, as it concerns those management-engineering oriented problems arising among:

1. Project personnel (line engineers)
2. Project personnel and project leaders
3. Project leaders and management

Engineers and scientists firmly agree that their R & D work cannot be managed in precisely the same way as manufacturing operations. Many of them clearly recognize their own glaring lack of understanding and grasp of managerial and administrative processes and objectives in terms of those economic-based factors such as project specification limits, facilities, time, and costs, all of which heighten the confusion.

Major problems confronting the project leader and closely related to the line engineers on the one hand, and the chief engineers on the other, are explored and spelled out in this book. In the final chapter specific recommendations relating to each of the defined problems are submitted, each with its considered analysis and evaluation. The recommendations for some of the defined problems should help alleviate them. But for some others, recommendations, analysis, and evaluation can help only to understand them and to cope with them more effectively.

I willingly accepted the assistance of many who unhesitatingly helped in suggesting sources of material and in the general preparation of the manuscript, but I implacably guarded my responsibility for organizing, developing, and presenting this book in its entirety. Should any of this material strike a discord, I can only ascribe it to my stubbornness, which, for better or for worse, prevailed throughout the course of the study.

Much of the credit for carrying on and bringing this study to completion I graciously give to my wife, Lillian. Her patience, encouragement, and spirit were overwhelmingly contagious.

I also owe much to my colleague and friend, Powell Niland, professor of management at Washington University, St. Louis, Missouri, whose comments were invaluable.

Finally, I feel that I may be uncompromisingly in debt to the reader. To those readers who feel they received some helpful suggestions, as well as to those who feel they derived little benefit, I offer caution or consolation that the ideas, concepts, and conclusions in this book are only, after all, the points of view of one person.

T. M.

New Brunswick, New Jersey
July 1963

Contents

Preface iii

1 . . **Introduction** 1
   Subject Matter and Scope of Study
   Aim of Study
   Presentation of Study Results

2 . . **The Research and Development Function in the Companies Studied** . . . 8
   What Did Management Expect from R & D?
   How R & D Work Was Done
   Flow of Work through R & D Function
   A Sample Project in the R & D Function
   Appendix: A Crash Program

3 . . **R & D Administration and Role of Budgeting in the Companies Studied** . . . 23
   How Management Administered R & D
   Role of Budgeting in R & D Administration
   Project Leader's Role in Administration—Use of Budgets
   Summary

4 . . **Standard Budgetary Process and the Role of the Project Leader** 36
   The Standard Budgetary Process
   Typical Role of Project Leader in Budgetary Process
   Summary

vii

5. Limitations to Project Leader's Use of Budgets ... 55
Limitations as Seen by Project Leader
Limitations of Project Leader as Seen by Chief Engineer
Limitations of Project Leader as Seen by Author
Summary

6. Low Predictability ... 67
Low Predictability and Uncertainty
Uncertainty in Forecasting Process for Budget
Forecasting in Production versus Forecasting in R & D
Summary

7. Planning and Scheduling in the Context of Low Predictability ... 72
Project Leader's Need for More Effective Planning
Project Leader's Need for a Scheduling Device
Implications
Summary

8. Organization and Communication ... 88
Project Leader and Responsibility for Project
Organizational Encumbrances
Implications
Summary

9. Monthly Project-Progress Review ... 95
Monthly Progress Review as a Communication Device
Implications
Summary

10. Recommendations ... 103
Recommended Changes in Budgetary Process
Recommendations to Project Leaders
Recommendations to Management (Chief Engineers)

11. Summary of Findings ... 133
Project Leader's Role in Budgeting
Limitations That Faced the Project Leader
Recommendations to Project Leader
Recommendations to Management
General Discussion
Summary

Bibliography ... 143

Index ... 145

▶▶▶▶ **1**

Introduction

Research and development (R & D) has become an important resource in the development of our economic, social, cultural, and political way of life. Through advancements in medicine, food technology, transportation, and communication, the standard of living has progressed markedly. In the past half century industrial growth has been incredible. Because of atomic energy and space explorations science has become a factor of incalculable importance in national and world-wide growth.

In 1940, the federal government spent approximately $74 million on R & D; in 1962 the expenditure was estimated to be over $10.2 billion,[1] and some authoritative sources have predicted that this amount will double over the next decade. Of the funds for the total R & D effort performed in industry in 1953, the federal government supplied 39 percent, increasing its contribution to 50 percent of total funds estimated for 1962.[2] Although private industry's relative contribution declined during this period, the absolute amount of private R & D investment skyrocketed. According to the National Science Foundation, the development phase has consumed consistently more than two-thirds of total R & D funds allocated to industry.

Of the grand total over-all national R & D effort (including federal government, profit organizations, educational institutions, and

[1]National Science Foundation, *Federal Funds for Science X* (NSF 61–82). Washington, D. C.: Government Printing Office, 1962, p. 40.

[2]*Ibid.*, p. 13. See also National Science Foundation, *Funds For Research and Development In Industry* (NSF 62–3). Washington, D. C.: Government Printing Office, 1959, p. 6; McGraw-Hill Department of Economics, *Business' Plans for New Plants and Equipment 1962/1965*, 15th Annual Survey. New York: McGraw-Hill Publishing Company, Inc., 1962, p. 9.

others) private industry was expected to perform 80 percent of the estimated 1962 effort ($12 billion out of $15 billion) while paying for only 40 percent of the total expenditures.[3] According to the McGraw-Hill series on research and development, the aircraft and parts, electrical machinery, and communications industries were expected to perform approximately 57 percent of the total industrial R & D effort ($6.9 billion out of $12 billion) estimated for 1962, while the chemical, machinery, instruments, and petroleum industries were to account for an estimated 20 percent.[4]

The main incentive for R & D expenditures by private industry is that it pays off. Economists and businessmen recognize the fact that R & D is related to profit, growth, and productivity. In 1928, in his theory of economic development, J. A. Schumpeter, the Austrian-born Harvard economist, stated that industrial growth is dependent on innovation (technology and the ability to translate technology into cash).[5] Both Joel Dean and Paul A. Samuelson, contemporary economists, state that R & D creates demand for capital and, hence, becomes a source for investments.[6] Moreover, the R & D program has become an important consideration in appraising a firm for investment purposes.[7] Many manufacturing firms are working continually on new products and new processes, and nearly all are working on improvements of existing ones. Within 25 years about half our working force will be working on products unknown today.

Clearly, then, R & D has become a major part of American business.

R & D is a costly and difficult undertaking, and its administration lacks the satisfactory control and management accorded to other functions of a company. An acceptable administrative process for R & D can come about only from a profound understanding of what is involved.

One way to visualize the field of R & D administration is to compare it with manufacturing, where results are predictable. In the

[3]National Science Foundation, *Federal Funds For Science X*, p. 20.
[4]McGraw-Hill Department of Economics, *op. cit.*, p. 9.
[5]J. A. Schumpeter, "The Instability of Capitalism," *Economic Journal*, September, 1928, pp. 377–378.
[6]Joel Dean, *Capital Budgeting*, 3d ed. Englewood Cliffs, N. J.: Prentice-Hall, Inc., 1956, p. 15. See also Paul A. Samuelson, *Economics*, 4th ed. New York: McGraw-Hill Book Company, Inc., 1955, p. 232.
[7]*R & D and The Investor*, survey on R & D programs. New York: Merrill Lynch, Pierce, Fenner & Smith, Inc., 1960. p. 3.

latter, profits and investments can be related and estimated with reasonable accuracy. Prime variables of production like labor, material, quality (yield), and equipment can be measured and evaluated in terms meaningful to management, such as return on investment, and productivity.

In R & D, appropriation of funds, area to be researched and engineered, budgeting, and performance measurement are not entirely measurable or conducive to satisfactory evaluation. The work-measurement techniques of manufacturing cannot be applied because R & D results are derived primarily from the engineering ingenuity of individuals. In production, work plans and rates of output are predicted with greater certainty, whereas in engineering the information needed to predict is oftentimes the objective of the research and development endeavor.

Budgeting is commonly defined as a financial expression of the planned work operations of a firm and can be expressed in nondollar terms such as production units and/or man-hours.[8] In manufacturing, budgeting is a formalized method for consolidating, coordinating, and planning operations.[9] While budgeting is useful in the planning of an R & D program, it has questionable value in the control of R & D costs and the measurement and evaluation of R & D output;[10] its chief benefits for R & D lie in the achievement of a balanced program and the coordination of the program with other company plans. "Planning of programs and control of finances represent the most generally accepted methods by which management of an R & D establishment can maintain effective direction of the over-all effort of the laboratory."[11]

Subject Matter and Scope of Study

The subject matter of this study concerns the project leader's role and the budgetary process as they pertain to the work of a laboratory in the semiconductor field of the electronics industry. Typically, the spectrum of scientific and engineering activities con-

[8]David R. Anderson, *Practical Controllership*. Homewood, Ill.: Richard D. Irwin, Inc., 1951, p. 102.
[9]Clarence B. Nickerson, *Cost Accounting*. New York: McGraw-Hill Book Company, Inc., 1954, p. 9.
[10]George W. Howard, *Common Sense in Research and Development Management*. New York: Vintage Books, Inc., 1955, p. 56.
[11]James B. Quinn, "How Industry Uses R & D Budgets," *The Management Review*. New York: American Management Association, Inc., 1959, p. 56.

stituting industrial R & D consists of pure research, applied research, development and design engineering, and pilot production.

Pure Research. The purpose of pure research is to search for knowledge for the sake of knowing. In research laboratories new ideas and concepts are created and proved to be scientifically sound and logical. In most scientific work the end objectives of the next experiment depend on the results of the preceding ones, which makes the prediction of results beyond the immediate experiments highly uncertain.

Applied Research. Beyond pure research is the task of determining to what product, new or old, a new idea can be applied. Search for scientific information that is needed to develop a salable product is called applied research.

Development and Design Engineering. In product development-and-design engineering the basic scientific concepts and related information are already available. Thus it is possible to predetermine a series of dependent and independent experiments necessary for the development of the whole or any part of product specifications. Based on the immediately preceding results, each experiment is improvised and changed until "success" is reached. Guessing the number of experiments needed for success is reasonably accurate. Once a certain degree of reproducibility is reached, the product specifications are frozen.

Pilot Production. Next, in a pilot-run phase, a number of production runs are made to test the entire product specifications; upon achievement of satisfactory results, the product is transferred to the factory. Pilot facilities usually are maintained as a control against the beginning factory-production run and serve as an acceptable model to judge controversies over manufacturing methods and product design that may arise between the factory and development engineering.

Phase of R & D Coming under Study The variety of sciences and engineering specialties involved in a typical R & D laboratory is determined by the character of the industry and the requirements of the company. In the electronics field the R & D work is multidisciplinary, particularly in the semiconductor area, which involves chemistry, metallurgy, physics, and electrical and mechanical engineering, and the integration of these various sciences and engineering disciplines results in an R & D spectrum of great complexity. This study is centered on the development engineering phase of R & D in the semiconductor field of the electronics industry.

Because of the state of the art of R & D administration, there is no definite organizational line separating applied research from product development-and-design engineering (pure research, however, is generally performed apart from the rest of the company organizationally as well as geographically). In semiconductor development engineering, 90 percent of the early stages of project work is applied research, but after some progress has been made, the work becomes 80 percent development engineering. Though some scientists, in contrast to engineers, are assigned to do either pure research or applied research only, development engineers do varying degrees of applied research in addition to their regular engineering effort. This study therefore involves both applied research and development engineering phases of the R & D effort.

Organizational Level Coming under Study In addition, this study does not concern itself with every echelon of the organizational structure of an R & D laboratory but centers on the project level; the two principal representatives of management involved at this level are the chief engineer and the project leader.

At the top management and chief engineer levels the objectives and responsibilities are broad in nature, involving the appropriation of sums of money, its allocation to well-selected projects, the allocation of manpower, the concern with morale and working climate necessary to foster creative work, and over-all results and the integration of these results with manufacturing and sales.

Typically, the chief engineer is in charge of the whole of development engineering, being responsible for all project engineers, and for planning, coordinating, and directing engineering activities of the laboratory. Budgeting — that is, the development and use of the budget — is one of his responsibilities. The level of management above the chief engineer has final approval of his budgetary decisions and, to this extent, is part of the over-all budgetary process.

At the core of the budgetary process for the laboratory is the allocation of resources within the individual engineering projects. It is the responsibility of the project leader to dovetail the various project activities so as to complete the work reasonably within the allocated money and timetable limits set by management.

Aim of Study

The project level constitutes a vital area in administration — management's efforts, money, and facilities are directed at the project work that flows from the engineer's bench. Success or failure of R & D effort depends on how projects are planned and implemented. In many instances, even under the direction of able researchers, project work stalls and eventually is completed in a state of confusion. This confusion is largely attributable to ineffective planning due to the uncertainty in R & D and the lack of administrative know-how of those key technical personnel directing the project.

The basic purpose of this study is to describe and characterize the role of the project leader in the budgetary process.

The project leader, at the lowermost rung of the management ladder, is both R & D engineer and manager. In general it is not easy for the project leader to plan and coordinate activities efficiently because of the uncertainties in R & D work. It is also likely that the project leader does not have management training and therefore lacks management skills. Through planning and coordinating, the project leader aims to achieve efficient use of engineering manpower and thereby to produce project results. Maximum, meaningful use of engineering time gives maximum output, minimizing delays. Though other planning devices are available, proper budgeting minimizes the waste of resources and is a good planning tool for the project leader. Improving the usefulness of budgeting to the project leader would ultimately benefit top management. Specifically, then, this study is addressed to the following questions:

1. How effective is budgeting as a management tool to the project leader?
2. What can and should be done to make the budget more useful (effective) to the project leader?

Presentation of Study Results

The uncertainties of R & D administration and the wide and free range of attitude and thinking, as well as the inherent behavioral differences in people, suggested that more than one company should be studied. Actually, three separate companies participated, making possible exhaustive interviews with nine project leaders (three from each company laboratory), three chief engineers (one from each company), and the detailed examination of three budgetary processes.

The R & D function, which is the sum total of all project work and the object of R & D administration, is subject to budgeting; hence, to provide a better comprehension of the usefulness of budgeting to the project leader and management, the R & D function and

R & D administration are described in the initial chapters. The R & D function is described by showing the following:

1. What management expects from R & D
2. How R & D work is done
3. A description of the laboratory organization
4. A description of a typical project

In discussing R & D administration, the following management decisions are described:

1. Type and size of laboratory organization and allocation of manpower to projects
2. Procedures for financial control, including the appropriation of funds for R & D, its allocation to projects, project selection, and checking up on progress

The synthesis of a typical budgetary process and typical role of the project leader, derived from the actual observations, follows, showing how the budget is developed and used.

In the ensuing chapters the limitations facing the project leader in the budgetary process are defined and analyzed with supporting evidence. The final chapter presents recommendations based on an evaluation of the limitations pertaining to the coordination of project work and engineering manpower, and the ways and means of making the budget a more useful management tool for both the project leader and management.

▶▶▶▶ **2**

The R & D Function in the Companies Studied

In this study the subject matter of budgeting is the R & D function and the requirements of that function. Since budgeting is a planning device, the project leader's coordination and planning of work is part and parcel of the subject of budgeting. In order to provide a better basis for understanding the problems of budgeting in this context, the R & D function and how it was typically accomplished in the case of three individual companies is described.

What Did Management Expect from R & D?

Transistors: General Description and Product Line The typical laboratory observed in this investigation was involved in the research and development of the transistor. This electronic device amplifies electrical signals many hundreds of times and does the work of many types of standard vacuum tubes more efficiently. Transistors are capable of operating at very low and very high frequencies and of operating under extreme temperature conditions ranging up to approximately 200° F for germanium-type transistors and higher for the silicon-type devices. Two of the main advantages of the transistor over the vacuum tube are that it is much smaller in over-all geometry (it is about the size of a thumbnail), and that it is made of many fewer parts.

There are fundamentally two kinds of transistors, one made of silicon and the other of germanium.[1] For each kind there are basically

---

[1] Pure (98 percent) crystalline germanium (Ge) is a true semiconductor and has properties intermediate between those of metals and nonmetals. It contains small traces of impurities (antimony, tin, aluminum, and phosphorus). At low temperatures, electrons from impurity atoms cause electrical conduction, and at high temperatures resistivity decreases.

Pure (98 percent) silicon (Si), which has a nonmetallic lattice structure like Ge, has electrical characteristics and operates at 400° F, approximately 200° F higher than Ge.

three different model types. The junction-type transistor is made by the metallurgical joining of three separate materials, one of which is either silicon or germanium, with each material having different chemical and metallurgical properties. The diffused type is similar to the junction type except that the separate materials are diffused or welded together.[2] The third type is a grown crystal. One way of growing such a crystal is by allowing the end of a rod of germanium or silicon to drip into the shape of a teardrop in a high-temperature, electronic furnace. The center horizontal slice, because of its desirable metallurgical, chemical, and electrical characteristics, is diced, each solid piece (1/64 inch square) becoming a transistor with the input, output, and ground leads attached to the appropriate faces. The diffused and grown-type transistors operate at respectively higher frequencies and temperatures.

The companies studied sold both silicon and germanium transistors, each available in from 20 to 30 model types. Prices ranged from $1 to $20 per unit with the power and frequency characteristics increasing directly with the price. Transistors were used in many types of communication devices, computers, radar, and guided missiles.

What Management Expected The work of the laboratories examined was divided into projects, each with a management-written technical proposal describing the desired objectives. The complexities of the multi-disciplinary nature of the laboratory work did not lessen management's expectations from the laboratories, which were as follows:

1. To make a "Chinese copy" of an existing transistor in order to stay abreast of competition
2. To improve existing products
3. To develop new products and methods
    a. New for company
    b. New for industry

The ideas for project work emerged from the sales force and from the laboratory personnel.

[2]The diffused portion of the semiconductor material, itself having a different metallurgical lattice (molecular) structure, enhances the amplification qualities of the transistor.

How R & D Work Was Done

Generally, the project team, through the individual efforts of member engineers, is responsible for achieving the technical proposal objectives.[3] The work of the line engineers, each representing a scientific discipline, or function, is coordinated usually by a project leader.

Laboratory Organization Each of the laboratories of this study was part of the larger organizational unit called a division which, in addition to the R & D work, was responsible for manufacturing, sales and financial control of the entire semiconductor operations (Figure 2-1, A).

Management generally has a choice of three types of laboratory organization structure:[4]

1. Functional, or subject-oriented, with project teams within functions
2. Functional with project teams cutting across functional lines
3. Project-oriented

In both the first and second types of organization, the laboratory is divided into functional organization units according to subject area, such as chemistry, physics, electrical engineering, and mechanical engineering. If the technical work does not cut across functional lines, it becomes the responsibility of the functional supervisor in whose function the work falls. The technical work is assigned to either one individual or a group of engineers (called a team) within the functional unit. The functional head is responsible to management for the supervision of the work, and he in turn holds the team leader responsible for the coordination of the work.

If the technical work cuts across functional lines because of its interdisciplinary nature, a group of engineers, each representing one of the needed subject areas, is organized into a project team. A project leader, an engineer from one of the functions, is designated to coordinate the interdisciplinary activities of the project; he does not, how-

---

[3]The team system was usually used in cases where the project work involved two or more disciplines. For more details concerning project or organization, see George W. Howard, *Common Sense in R & D Management*. New York: Vintage Books, Inc., 1955, p. 20.

[4]George W. Howard, *op. cit.*, p. 15. See also Robert N. Anthony, *Management Controls in Industrial Research Organization*. Cambridge: Harvard University Printing Office, 1952, p. 38.

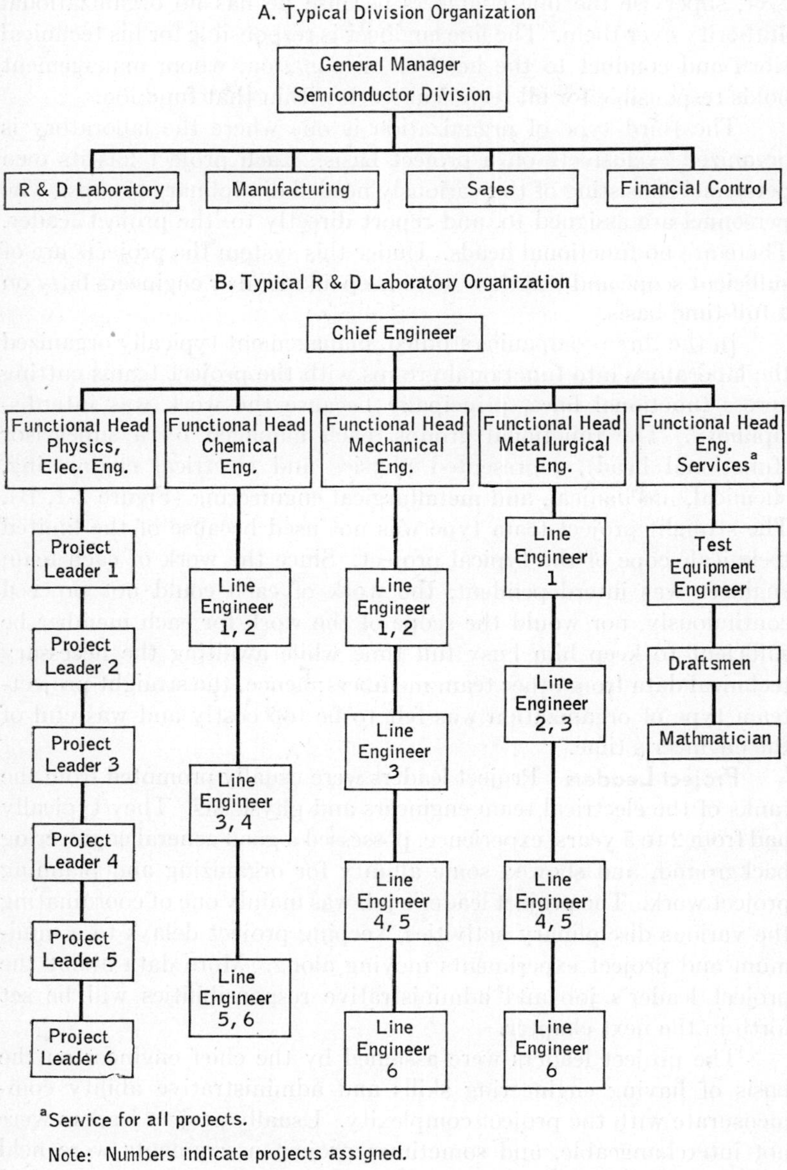

How R & D Work Was Done

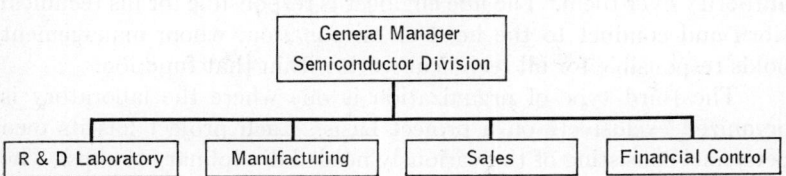

^aService for all projects.

Note: Numbers indicate projects assigned.

FIGURE 2-1. Organizational structure of the division and the R & D laboratory.

ever, supervise the line engineers because he has no organizational authority over them. The line engineer is responsible for his technical work and conduct to the head of his function, whom management holds responsible for all technical work within that function.

The third type of organization is one where the laboratory is organized exclusively on a project basis. Each project has its own personnel consisting of the variously needed disciplinary groups. The personnel are assigned to, and report directly to, the project leader. There are no functional heads. Under this system the projects are of sufficient scope and length so as to keep all member engineers busy on a full-time basis.

In the three companies studied, management typically organized the laboratory into functional groups with the project teams cutting across functional lines, principally because the work was interdisciplinary. The functional groups, each managed by a supervisor (functional head), represented physics and electrical engineering, chemical, mechanical, and metallurgical engineering (Figure 2-1, B). The straight project-team type was not used because of the limited technical scope of the typical project. Since the work of each team engineer was interdependent, the work of each could not proceed continuously, nor would the scope of the work for each member be sufficient to keep him busy full time while awaiting the necessary technical data from other team members; hence, the straight project-team type of organization was felt to be too costly and wasteful of the engineer's time.

Project Leaders Project leaders were usually promoted from the ranks of the electrical team engineers and physicists. They typically had from 2 to 5 years' experience, possessed a good general engineering background, and showed some affinity for organizing and planning project work. The project leader's job was mainly one of coordinating the various disciplinary activities, keeping project delays to a minimum and project experiments moving along. More data about the project leader's job and administrative responsibilities will be set forth in the next chapter.

The project leaders were assigned by the chief engineer on the basis of having engineering skills and administrative ability commensurate with the project complexity. Usually project leaders were not interchangeable, and sometimes project assignments were held awaiting the "right" engineer. The project leaders also "doubled in brass," serving for some purposes as line engineers.

Line Engineers Project team members were called line engineers, each representing a particular functional area and each reporting to a supervisor of that function. The job of the line engineer was to plan and carry out his experiments, and after interpretation of results, to plan and implement the next set of experiments. Each line engineer was responsible for the materials and equipment necessary for his experiments as well as for the cooperation with others demanded by the interdisciplinary nature and interdependency of the work. The project leader was instrumental in providing a good basis for the all-important communications system and in striving for conducive human relations among project personnel.

A line engineer was assigned to a project jointly by his functional supervisor and the chief engineer, with some weight given to the engineer's request. Line engineers were not interchangeable, and therefore it was not always possible to assign the engineer best suited for a project because of an existing assignment.

Chief Engineer The chief engineer was in charge of the entire laboratory and was responsible for its direction, coordination, and control. Together with higher management he was responsible for determining the project work load, and solely, he was responsible to higher management for getting the work done within the limits of the available allocated resources. To the laboratory personnel the chief engineer was manager and the one who ultimately settled any of the technical and/or management problems. His administrative responsibilities and operating procedures are discussed in the next chapter.

Functional Group Heads The functional heads (engineers themselves) were responsible for the line engineers in their groups. With approval from the chief engineer they assigned their engineers to projects and helped them plan, carry out, and appraise the technical results of project experiments. Together with the chief engineer they established the priority rank of projects and scheduled each line engineer's time over the several projects to which he was assigned. Functional heads were not responsible for projects as a whole, but only for that portion of the technical work to which their respective line engineers were assigned.

Flow of Work through R & D Function

Total Number of Projects — Projects per Line Engineer On the average, the number of projects in process at any one time was from

5 to 8 and each ranged from 4 to 24 months in duration. All disciplinary areas were needed in the typical project, with some requiring more engineering time than others.

The line engineers usually worked on at least 2 and sometimes 3 projects simultaneously. They were not assigned to give their full time to one project because of the intermittent nature of the experimental work owing to the dependency on results coming from the other disciplines. A full-time assignment to one project tended to increase the line engineer's idle time in waiting for these other results. Since the engineering labor cost on a project averaged about 70 percent of total project cost, careful use of the engineer's time was desirable.

Laboratory Facilities The basic capital equipment consisted of chemical laboratory facilities, electronic microscopes and photographic equipment, electric furnaces, and electric test equipment. The budget for capital equipment was formulated by the chief engineer and submitted to top management for approval. The equipment was shared by all projects and the allocation of using time was set by the functional head responsible for the equipment. The priority rank of the projects set by the chief engineer resolved scheduling conflicts in most instances.

Services Requisitions for material and hardware, and work orders to company machine shops and outside vendors under $200 were processed by project personnel without chief engineer approval. Each laboratory had engineering drafting services and technical assistance from company specialists such as a mathematician or physical chemist. Sometimes, if provision had been made in project plans, services of outside engineering and scientific consultants were secured.

A Sample Project in the R & D Function

A good understanding of the nature of a typical project is provided by the Appendix to this chapter. The fact that the sample project is one involving great urgency creates some unusual problems, but they can be readily identified. In fact, the urgency of this project, entitled *Crash*, serves to highlight some of the basic elements of team administration. The purpose of "Crash" was to develop a "Chinese copy" of a transistor called X, already being promoted by other competitors.

Crash Program versus Regular Program "Crash" was a typical project as to its technical proposal, number of subprojects, and disciplines involved, and differed only in the way it was scheduled in the laboratory (see Table 2-1). Because of the urgent need to stay abreast of competition, the project was processed through the laboratory on a crash basis by being queued ahead of other projects on laboratory facilities and being assigned the full amount of the line engineer's time, not just a share of it. Had the project been scheduled on a regular basis, completion in all likelihood would have taken 10 months.

Crash projects differed from regular projects in that several likely solutions to the problem (experiments) were run in parallel, as against the usual practice of running the most likely solutions in tandem. In crash programming usually there were no reruns of experiments because a reasonable number of the most likely solutions were tried simultaneously. Under regular conditions alternative experiments were run only if previous experiments failed.

Uncertainty Table 2-1 also shows that the probability of technical success within the limits of the allocated resources for project "Crash" ranged from 80 to 99 percent for all but one of the subprojects. The lower probability for subproject C was due to the lack of company experience in combining and directing the existing theoretical knowledge toward new applications. By "combining" knowledge is meant the correct understanding and association of the existing scientific theory with the project technological objectives in order to design an effective method of solution. Uncertainty was present in the following ways:

1. In the interpretation of the theory
2. In relating it to project goals
3. In the actual design and application of experiments

Other factors also contributed to the uncertainty:

1. How accurately were the problems defined?
2. Could the method of solution chosen bring about the desired results? (Depended upon ability and experience of line engineer and generally on the know-how of others in the laboratory.)

Project success is obtained when the technical objectives of the project proposal are achieved. As each experiment draws closer to the

TABLE 2-1
Information Concerning Sample Project X

A. *Project Technical Proposal*

Develop a transistor to be called X, a "Chinese copy" of a transistor made by other companies.

1. Diffused type
2. Germanium composition
3. Operating frequency 1000 megacycles

B. *Project Breakdown*

Sub-project (task)	Disciplinary function	Number of engineers[a]	Probability of success within timetable limits of project (in percent)	Degree of previous experience
A	Metallurgy	1	80	Considerable
B	Chemistry	1	80	Considerable
C	Physical chemistry	1	50	Less experience and knowledge; have basic "chemistry," need new combination of knowledge
D	Physics	(same man as in C)	99	Considerable
E	Mechanical engineering	1	97	Considerable
F	Chemistry	(same man as in B)	97	Considerable
G	Electrical engineering	1	80	Considerable

[a] Manpower distribution (total project): Full-time line engineers..... 5
Technical assistants........ 6
Total manpower   11

project technological objectives, the probability of success generally increases with each succession of experiments, and the predictability of chances for achieving project goals is gauged on this.

As for project X, the chief engineer claimed that he had about a 70 percent chance to meet the project timetable schedule and over an 80 percent chance to meet the budget. He ascribed this to the uncertainty in subproject C in which there was an estimated 50–50 chance for achieving success on the first round of experiments. As the planned schedule shows in Figure 2-2, the chief engineer did not show the possibility of running subproject C beyond the first run of experiments,

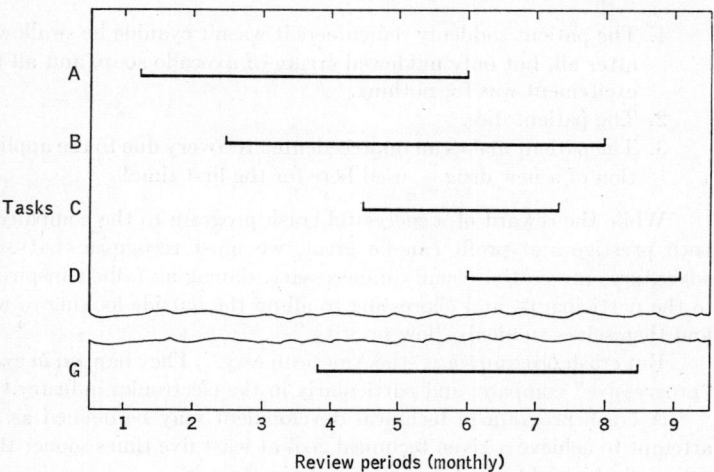

FIGURE 2-2. Calendar time (in months)/project tasks under ordinary programming.

though, faced with failure, either another run would have been performed or the project technological objectives lowered. A breakthrough in subproject C mentioned in "Crash" brought the project to completion on schedule.

Appendix: A Crash Program

Crash![5]

As if industrial laboratories didn't have enough trouble trying to carry out ordinary research and development programs and making them

[5]This section was contributed by an experienced senior engineer.

remotely take on the appearance of even partial success — they must also cope with the sudden emergency of the crash program.

A crash program is simultaneously agonizing and fascinating, ulcer-making and satisfying. It is never dull; it is always exciting with the special sort of excitement that is continually flirting with frustration.

The "crasher" is like a hard-luck ambulance driver rushing his deathly sick passenger to the hospital. Even with police escort, he encounters a thousand roadblocks: slow-moving trucks cut into his path; pedestrians pause in the middle of the street; dogs chase him; traffic jams occur at every turn; and somehow — a thing that never occurred before — he gets a flat tire half way to the hospital.

Finally, he arrives at the hospital and one of three things happens:

1. The patient suddenly remembers it wasn't cyanide he swallowed after all, but only mildewed cream of avocado soup, and all the excitement was for nothing.
2. The patient dies.
3. The patient makes an unprecedented recovery due to the application of a new drug — used here for the first time!

While the reward of a successful crash program to the company in both prestige and profit can be great, we must recognize that such adventures are costly, usually unnecessary, damaging (albeit inspiring) to the participants, and depressing to all on the outside looking in who find themselves suddenly "low priority."

But crash programs are "the American way." They happen in every "progressive" company and particularly in the electronics industry.

A crash program in technical development may be defined as the attempt to achieve a given technical goal at least five times sooner than anyone in his right mind should expect to attain it.

Two factors are fixed:

1. The goal to be achieved
2. The available time

Nothing else is fixed; nothing else is stable. All else approaches chaos. Success can come only from bringing some semblance of order into the chaos. The following "ordering" conditions are necessary:

1. There must be a capable project leader and he must have a plan. The project leader must plan creatively and expeditiously; in fact, he must make such effective use of expedients, of what is "at hand," as to be more a tactician than a planner. The plan, plot, or tactic marshall all available forces and must foresee a maximum number of contingencies. Critical tasks of the plan deserve several parallel and simultaneous approaches. With this philoso-

Appendix: A Crash Program

phy, necessarily, a number of investigations will be abandoned in the end. This is all right; they were "insurance."
2. An experienced staff must be available that is skillful in the subtasks, the successful conclusion of which must constitute the building blocks for the finished project. All members of this group must take a pledge for the "duration" — "No technical prejudices"; time enough for that later.
3. There must be an established array of equipment capable of being adopted to this project (although some equipment is necessarily lacking).
4. Raw material must be available (although some material must be flown in from, shall we say, Seattle).
5. At least one member of the "crash" group must be ingenious.
6. One "crasher" must be a historical company character who knows where all the underground passageways and overhead catwalks lead. He loves to prowl in the limbo warehouses of equipment and he can usually come up with a transformer or furnace discarded in 1943 which is "just the thing."
7. Finally, success or failure is insured by the quality of the expeditor and messenger service. When the time scale gets really critical, this job is entrusted to no one lower than Division Manager or Laboratory Chief status.

While all the factors mentioned are necessary and important and a case may be made for each as the crucial point, it is (1) that most deserves expansion and detailed treatment here.

Planning might be defined for our purpose as setting up technical directions to reach a given objective with minimum cost and under a given set of boundary conditions. Generally there will be no major difficulty in designing a project schedule fulfilling the given conditions provided the project objective is intrinsically feasible. Accordingly, before the plan is put forth, there must be some assurance of feasibility; an axiom for predicting feasibility in a crash program may be given:

If an objective is predicted to be attainable under *ideal* conditions, it will also be attainable under crash conditions.

Once feasibility has been predicted, the project leader must examine the universe of his laboratory, its equipment and its personnel, and square this against those factors in the project that permit no compromise as well as those that allow some leeway. At this point the actual project schedule will be set up and it is here that the time limit set to reach the objective will determine the character of the project schedule. Generally a project schedule is a presentation of the efforts involved in solving the partial problems as a function of time, and graphically may have the appearance of Figure 2-2. While the breaking up of the major objective into partial objectives will be common to what we shall call the normal and crash programs, the relative positions of the partial tasks on the project schedule as well as their lengths and the manpower they represent will be entirely different (Figure 2-3). In particular their differences will manifest themselves in the crash program in the following:

1. Assignment of manpower for every task beyond the point of diminishing returns.
2. Setting back as far as possible the starting time of every task. This means that task B, which should be based on the results of task A, will, nevertheless, start before the conclusion of that task, assuming success for A. Of course, in this way a certain amount of risk is introduced, since the results of A may not come out as

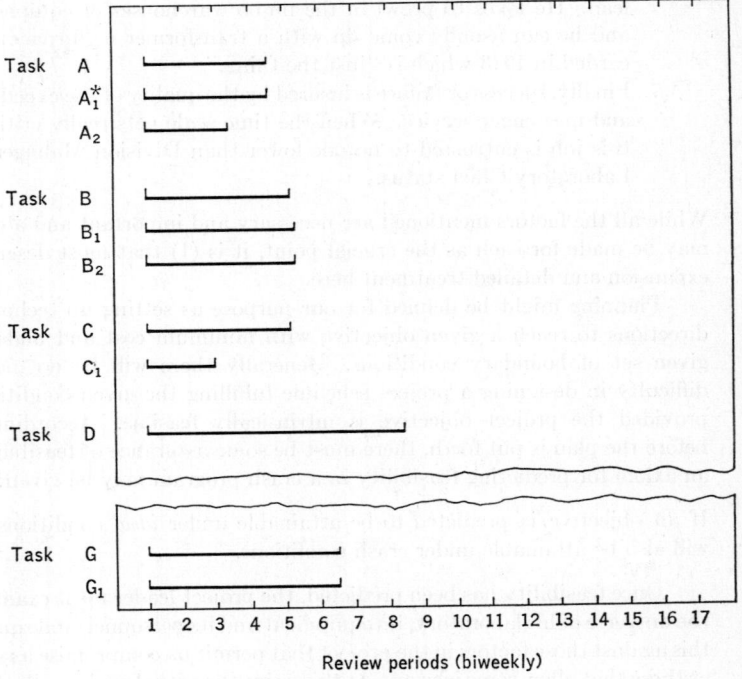

* Subscripts indicate task forces working on alternate solutions.

FIGURE 2-3. Calendar time (in biweekly periods)/project tasks under crash program.

expected; but on the other hand, rapid simultaneous conclusions of A and B will save considerable time.
3. Providing alternative solutions to problems whose chances of successful solution within the given time appear slim by setting up parallel task forces handling the alternative tasks.
4. Shortening review periods as compared with normal programs so as to provide the necessary added flexibility and control; this is particularly important in the crash program because of the fact that the relatively short times involved reduce the possibility of useful feedback information to adjust the direction of development.

As in a normal program, a certain amount of uncertainty involved in estimating the budget can sometimes be eliminated by assigning a relatively small budget for exploratory experiment. This may help to establish at least the upper limit on budget requirement. Obviously the savings in time accomplished will be strongly reflected in the budget in terms of requirements on man-hours, equipment, and material. The more emphasis there is on time-saving, however, the less efficient use can be made of any of these. Still, the price paid in the crash program is, by definition, considered not excessive due to the pertinent commercial or military exigencies.

Some time ago the Semiconductor Division of an electronics company instituted a crash program with the objective of developing a new transistor and of submitting a number of operable units within a period of 8 weeks. A short description of the planning and execution of this program may illustrate the points made above.

The project was broken down into four main tasks, three of which involved parallel or "insurance" variations. Thus a total of seven separate tasks were scheduled. On reviewing the seven individual tasks involved, it was noted that there was substantial experience in the laboratory in six of the tasks but none in the seventh. It is interesting to note that where experience existed it served mainly in the planning stage to point up its own seeming inadequacy. In spite of these facts, the conclusion was then reached that all individual objectives but the one appeared feasible, although with a relatively high degree of uncertainty of success within the short time. It was apparent that the solution of the one obvious major problem could not be found by techniques known at the company during the time available unless an "invention" were made. That is, it was reluctantly conceded that a new idea had to be conceived.

It is an interesting (and distressing) reflection on crash programs that by their nature they tend to stifle originality. Basic new ideas are avoided because they take more time to exploit than ideas that have already been partially exploited previously. However, as basic originality is stifled, qualities of ingenuity and skill in tactics of maneuvering of man-hours, equipment, and fragments of knowledge are brought to the fore.

At any rate, there was no choice but to generate a new idea. This was done (with strong feelings of guilt) and sheepishly a few exploratory experiments were made to try it out. The idea turned out to be satisfactory and one of the engineers received a patent bonus.

In the end the project was successful — by late Friday afternoon of the eighth week! This leads to the inevitable conclusion that success could also have been achieved late Friday of the seventh week or the sixth, these goals being really no more ridiculous than the eighth-week goal. We will pursue this avenue of thought no farther, but leave it instead to fester in the mind of the reader.

Generally it will be noticed that maximum flexibility and coordination are the prerequisites of such a crash program, which means that planning of the program is not completed on setting up the project schedule; in fact, it is not complete until the objectives of the project are reached. Here in particular, planning is a dynamic process that goes along with the execution of plans, both mutually adjusting themselves in the course of the process until the end of the program.

As was obvious from the beginning, a crash program demands good teamwork. In this case quite a number of intricate problems had to be solved separately by a number of individuals. The failure of any one of these subtasks would have meant failure of the complete project. This is an intriguing aspect of the crash program; it not only demands the proper spirit for teamwork, it also creates it.

And what happens when the crash program is over? Whether the goal was attained or not, there is an inevitable letdown. Reaping the benefits of the program, if any, and recouping from it constitute the biggest challenges to the project leader — bigger even than the successful attainment of the emergency goal.

▶▶▶▶ **3**

R & D Administration and Role of Budgeting in the Companies Studied

The purpose of this chapter is to provide a basis for understanding the project leader's typical budgetary problems as they occurred in the companies observed in this study. To gain a better understanding of budgeting and its uses, R & D administration must be understood, since budgeting is an administrative tool useful in the management process. In the preceding chapter the R & D function was described. In this chapter we will look at how management typically administered R & D and how management used budgets in making some of the key decisions. The project leader's role in R & D administration and his uses of the budget will also be developed.

How Management Administered R & D

Some of management's key decisions in laboratory administration observed in this study were as follows:

1. Organization (selection of type)
2. Size in terms of number of engineers
3. Allocation of engineers to project work
4. Major controls for R & D
5. Amount of annual dollar outlay to R & D
6. Allocation of dollars to projects
7. Checking up on expenditures
8. Cutoff
9. Project selection

In the ensuing discussion the chief engineer will be considered part of management, but in some instances he will be singled out for purposes of clarity.

23

Number of Engineers for Laboratory — Allocation to Projects

The total number of engineers for the laboratory and their allocation to projects depended on the following:

1. Availability of engineers in tight labor market
2. Work load of laboratory (number of projects)
3. Project calendar timetables
4. Amount of money appropriated for laboratory and its allocation to projects

Generally many companies are faced with the national shortage of engineers. The companies in this study, along with many others, have to evaluate their work load planning in terms of their ability to acquire the needed number of engineers.

The number of engineers needed in the examined companies was proportional to the work load of the projects within the laboratory. If this work load, expressed in man-hours, was held fixed and the elapsed time for conducting the project stretched out, then fewer engineers were needed to do the work. The altering of the completion date was dependent upon the necessity for dovetailing with sales promotional plans.

The number of engineers was also dependent on the rate at which the allocable funds were applied. With the total amount of funds fixed, the rate of use of funds varied with changes in the calendar timetable as illustrated by the following equation:

$$\frac{\text{total dollars}}{\text{calendar timetable (in months)}} = \text{dollar amount allocated per month}$$

In planning for manpower, management wanted to be reasonably sure that the net number of engineers needed was realistically attainable. In addition, management wanted to be reasonably sure that enough money was appropriated to finance the needed number of engineers. Layoffs threatened the security-mindedness of engineers and the company's recruiting effort; management therefore tried to keep a steady manpower level without downward fluctuations.

The number of engineers is related to and is part of the subject matter in a later section of this chapter dealing with the amount of money needed for R & D. To avoid repetition, the procedure for determining the number of engineers and their allocation to projects will be discussed in that section.

Conducive Working Climate Management of the companies studied typically believed that the working environment had a direct relationship with the quality and productivity of the laboratory's output. Even though the project team was responsible for achieving the technical objectives, nevertheless the major contributions in the engineering work were results of individual endeavour. In management's opinion factors such as a sound salary guide, extensive facilities and services, challenging work, opportunity for professional growth, and professional recognition, to mention only a few, were important in developing a conducive working climate. Clearly, each of these factors was geared to the individual. For example, management took great effort to match technical work to the man in order to develop the element of challenge. In providing a model shop within the laboratory, which was additional capacity, the line engineers were able to get small jobs done more quickly without going through the company's regular machine shop. Management fostered professional growth and development by encouraging participation in professional societies by paying for memberships and trips to meetings. Management typically provided professional services for the acquisition of patents, giving the individual engineer recognition for the invention.

The typical project leader influenced the working climate because it was his responsibility to coordinate the interdisciplinary activities of the project personnel and to foster cooperation. Management was reluctant to impose tight time schedules and budgets because of their inherent pressures on the engineers. Instead, management depended on a pledge of best effort from the project team to keep within budgeted man-hours and timetable limits. The project personnel were interested more in getting the technical work accomplished than in the processes of budgeting.

How Management Controlled R & D Some of the major factors directly related to the performance of the R & D function in the laboratories observed in this study were as follows:

1. "Brain quality" of project personnel
2. Organizational requirements (efficient allocation of resources — man-hours, time, and money)
3. Project selection
4. Project and/or subproject experiment cutoff

"Brain Quality" of Project Personnel. Each of the chief engineers

and project leaders interviewed expressed his feeling that technical know-how, or ability, was one of the most important factors governing the quality of project results. Each felt that the quality of performance could be no better than the men doing the work. Astute technical know-how provided a better basis for defining problems as well as for setting up methods for their solution and effectively interpretating the ensuing results. That this attitude is widely held has been attested to by Professor E. Grovenstein: "While many scientists may owe their greatness to their skill in choosing problems . . . , the significance [of their contributions] . . . depends on their peculiar quality of imagination . . . ."[1]

The chief engineers and project leaders also pointed to the importance of a proper working climate for bringing out the best in the line engineers. A proper working atmosphere was a factor given great importance by industrial research and development people. Mr. P. Salzberg, Director of the Chemical Department of du Pont, has stated, "The research (development) scientist must be provided with an environment that will stimulate his best efforts."[2]

The chief engineers of the laboratories studied felt that hiring better men was one way to control good quality project work, but they realized this was difficult to do in the face of the national engineer-shortage problem. They encouraged their engineers to participate in professional societies by giving papers, to take part in company and out-of-company seminars, and to take technical courses at the university level. These approaches generally seem to be the practices of many companies.[3] Mr. Salzberg, who was quoted above, further states, "But recruiting is only a start. . . . He [the engineer] should be given the opportunity to publish the technical results of high scientific caliber . . . ."[4]

Organizational Requirements (Budgets). Management of the laboratories studied typically gave much attention to making work plans and budgeting funds needed to do the technological work.

[1] Erling Grovenstein, Jr., "Some Factors in the Choice of Basic Research Problems in Science," *The Research Engineer*, Georgia Tech Engineering Experiment Station, July, 1956, p. 8.
[2] Paul L. Salzberg, "Progress Through Coordinated Effort," *Getting The Most from Product Research and Development*, Special Report No. 6. New York: American Management Association, 1955, p. 23.
[3] G. W. Howard, *Common Sense in R & D Management*. New York: Vintage Books, Inc., 1955, p. 33.
[4] Paul L. Salzberg, *op. cit.*, p. 36.

They planned the amount of money needed chiefly to make sure that they did not spend too much or too little, that the amount was in line with the division's sales and profits, and to make provision for having the money on hand as needed.

If insufficient funds were appropriated, the chances were that management would either defer or drop projects, lower project technical objectives, or appropriate more funds to continue the necessary work. If funds were not readily available, there would be greater pressure on management to plan more carefully and monitor costs and progress more thoroughly. If additional money was easily appropriated (and this practice was followed frequently), the chances for less careful use of resources was increased. With greater possibility of an extension of time and funds, there was a tendency for less care in the dovetailing of project activities and for less monitoring of budgeted costs.

Budgeting and scheduling are methods that helped management control financial expenditures and keep technical achievement within the limits of the appropriated funds. To stay within the over-all laboratory budget limits, management needed only to keep the number of engineers on the payroll at a fixed level and not allow overtime. This, however, did not assure the timely output of laboratory work and the completion of projects within the limits of the allocated resources. Management used monthly reports on technical progress compared against the technical work plan to judge if technical work was on schedule. By and large this appraisal pointed up the uncertainties of forecasting. The matter of budgets and progress reviews will be covered more fully in the next two chapters. Management in these companies recognized the value of more accurate appropriation of funds, more careful monitoring of costs, and better coordination and dovetailing of project work.

Project Selection. Project selection was another important consideration and means of control in these companies. If the technical requirements of selected projects were beyond the technical know-how of project personnel, then in all likelihood the results would fall short of technical goals. In this event it was also probable that before technical objectives were adjusted, technical experimentation would go beyond the point of diminishing returns and hence consume company resources in a wasteful way.

Management recognized the importance of the salability and quality of the end product when selecting projects because of the effects on profit and on company reputation and prestige. Management typically attempted to select projects with end products that had desirable returns on investment. In estimating a return on investment they developed a *pro forma* Profit and Loss (P & L) statement along with a forecast of the investment needed, a part of which was the estimated R & D expenditure, for each project in the selection process. The management process for project selection will be considered more fully in the next chapter.

The selection of work projects offered management another means of control over both the technical performance and the financial performance of the laboratory.

Cutoff. Another factor typically used by management in the companies observed in order to control technical, as well as financial, performance was *cutoff*. Cutoff meant the stopping of projects and/or the termination of experiments within the projects. All of the chief engineers interviewed stressed that cutoff was important in assuring the efficient use of resources. The underlying principle favoring expedient cutoff was to just meet the project goals and not go beyond. In addition, in the face of grave technical difficulties, work should be stopped and technical goals altered in order to avoid wasting company resources that could be better employed elsewhere. But if project work was cut off too soon, the opportunity for reaching the desired technical objective was prevented and the risk of stifling line engineer incentive was increased. Problems relating to cutoff will be more fully developed in the next chapter.

Role of Budgeting in R & D Administration

How Much Money for R & D

One of the basic issues confronting management in the firms visited was the question of how much money, in total, should be allocated for the research and development function. The purpose of this section is to demonstrate how the budgetary process was involved in making and remaking this decision.

It was typical policy in the three semiconductor divisions to have the laboratory's expenditures financed from the division's own sales revenues. Therefore, one reason management budgeted its annual expenditures for R & D was to help keep these expenditures in line with the division's sales and profits. In addition the annual budget was used for the following purposes:

1. To plan cash-flow requirements (for engineers' salaries, material expenditures, and other expenses) on a monthly basis

2. To control expenditures by monitoring actual costs against budgeted amounts

The total estimated annual expenditures for the laboratory broken down on a monthly basis was the annual budget for the laboratory. Stated a little differently, the annual budget needed to carry on the laboratory work was a function of calendar-monthly time periods. The detailed process for determining the budget will be described more fully in the next chapter. However, in this section some of the key decisions and procedures are defined.

As a beginning step, it was typical of management in these companies to make a rough estimate as a working guide for total money potentially available for the laboratory in the ensuing period (next fiscal year). To derive this estimate, management used a set of ratios (expenditures for laboratory as a percent of net sales and net profit) based on historical data obtained from the company's accounting and sales departments. From this point, then, management next determined if the planned project work could be accomplished with the money potentially available (based on estimates from the ratios).

First, an estimate for total dollars needed was made on a project-by-project basis. At this point management had two estimates of the total laboratory budget: one derived from ratios and representing money potentially available, the other from a project-by-project breakdown and representing money needed. In reconciling the difference, management was able to determine the final amount of money for the laboratory. The reconciliation basically developed out of the simple process of comparing one estimate with the other. If the total annual laboratory budget estimated on a project-by-project basis was greater than the estimated amount from ratios, management had the following alternatives:

1. To accept the greater estimate and appropriate more money if the economic outlook for the semiconductor division was good.
2. If additional funds were not available
    a. To spread out timetables and cut appropriate number of engineers.
    b. To drop projects and cut appropriate number of engineers.
    c. To lower technical objectives and cut appropriate number of engineers.

If the estimate from the project-by-project procedure was not greater than the one obtained from the ratios, then management had the following alternatives:

1. To make no adjustments.
2. To adjust completion dates to finish projects earlier and add appropriate number of engineers.
3. To add new projects and add appropriate number of engineers.
4. To add to the technical objectives and add appropriate number of engineers.

In any event, management then checked the feasibility of obtaining the incremental number of engineers needed. If this number of needed engineers was not obtainable, then management had a choice of the following:

1. To stretch out project timetables.
2. To drop or defer project(s).
3. To lower technical objectives.
4. To use overtime if funds were available.

The approved laboratory budget allocated over the calendar months became the cash-flow schedule showing working capital needs, and was also the standard against which actual costs were measured in checking up on expenditures. This procedure for estimating the annual dollar amount required for the laboratory, a part of the standard budgetary process (see next chapter), consumed several months in its development and involved estimates from and the cooperation of the chief engineer and managers of sales, manufacturing, and finance, under the general supervision of the manager of the semiconductor division. Because of the confidential nature of the information, management in the three firms visited did not show any examples revealing actual cost, sales, and profit data.

Checking up on R & D Expenditures A major concern for management during regular monthly review in the participating companies was to relate expenditures to technical progress in order to develop a basis for corrective action if necessary. To do this, management made a project-by-project analysis of budgeted versus actual costs. To get a more meaningful picture as to the effective use of resources, technical accomplishments were related to expenditures. Management's immediate problem was to determine if technical results were commensurate with expenditures. If technical goals were achieved within budget and calendar-time limits, then the project work was assumed to be in line with the expenditures and the schedule. The important question facing management was whether the remaining funds were adequate to complete the balance of project work.

Cutoff Decisions As described previously, cutoff was that point at which total project work and/or project experiments were stopped. The chief engineers claimed that even when planned technical objectives were reached, there was the strong urge on the part of project personnel to continue beyond this point to improve and refine what had already developed. They further stated that it was very difficult for line engineers to stop further work at this point because of their personal incentives of pride and interest. In fact, it has been found that the laboratory worker in industrial research and development organizations typically resisted cutoff.[5]

Cutoff was also considered by management during the monthly review period. In almost every project, management adjusted the technical objectives before the project was completed, the adjustments being based primarily on the increased technical knowledge gained from progress achieved during the project. Usually management initially set the technical goals slightly on the high side; therefore most of the time typical changes involved lowering the technical requirements. In making these technical changes, management was concerned with developing a product that was of a quality commensurate with the company's reputation and that would perform exactly as it was required to do to be salable. The underlying principle was not to give a Cadillac when a Ford was acceptable. When considering cutoff, management evaluated the following factors:

1. Probability of success in reaching desired objective (caliber of individuals involved a strong factor).
2. Proposed benefits from continued work versus cost.
3. Availability of enough funds to do continued work.
4. Other projects to which funds and personnel might be committed.

Essentially the decision boiled down to the balancing of the additional cost against anticipated benefits to the company. Management was also concerned with the effect on the project's timetable, especially during the later stages, because the project generally was scheduled

---

[5]Robert N. Anthony, *Management Controls in Industrial Research Organizations.* Cambridge, Mass.: Harvard University Press, 1952, p. 100.

for factory production at a given time, its timely output meshing with sales promotional activities. Information useful in making cutoff decisions came from several sources. The amount of remaining project funds came from monthly cost reports. The technical information on the continuance of work, such as the potential technical achievements and the probability of success, typically came from project personnel via the project leader's monthly reports. From these basic data management translated the continuance of work into additional calendar time and funds needed. General information that might be useful in making a cutoff decision flowed to management through regular organizational channels, namely, monthly cost reports and the project leader's monthly technical progress reports. When a particular cutoff was under consideration, however, more specific information if necessary was drawn from the same sources.

In general, a cutoff decision is a difficult one to make: because a technical breakthrough or achievement is always probable, a decision for cutoff is always at the risk of stifling the incentive of the project personnel.

Selecting the Project Project selection was typically one of the most important areas of management's responsibility because of its marked effect on the company's return on investment and on its position and reputation in the market.

Invariably management examined profitability for each new project under consideration. For new product development the accounting department, with the use of marketing data, forecasted a *pro forma* profit and loss statement covering the estimated economic life of the potential product. The investment side of this procedure included the project's R & D expenditures, its laboratory capital equipment expenditures, and any capital expenditures involving production facilities. This calculation could not have been made without the use of the project budget (R & D expenditures). The uncertainties in these forecasts made the return-on-investment calculation no better than the inherent estimates. Management typically did not give the return-on-investment estimate substantially more weight than the other factors when considering the selection of a project.

Although the company was in business to make a profit, return on investment was not always the governing factor in the selection process. At times a potential new product that did not have a comparable return on investment but fulfilled the need to broaden the company's line of products was selected because it helped maintain and promote the general sales level. Similarly, a project improving the quality of an existing product was selected because it promised to enhance the company's position and prestige.

The first step in the project selection procedure was to reject projects for which adequate technical know-how and ability did not exist. Then, all things being equal, return on investment, prestige and position in the market, and broadening of the line of products were, in the order given, the important factors taken into account.

Again, the companies interviewed did not give any examples of their return-on-investment calculations because of their confidential nature.

Project Leader's Role in Administration — Use of Budgets

The typical project leader's role in the administration of the laboratories in this study was to get his project started, to move the work along efficiently, and to bring it to completion. Fulfilling this role involved performing the following administrative tasks:

1. Programming the technical work
2. Checking up on work to keep it moving along as planned:
   a. Conducting monthly progress reviews and reporting to management
   b. Helping to decide corrective action
   c. Monitoring costs
3. Implementing management-approved changes to the project
4. Helping to estimate budget revisions
5. Encouraging and fostering teamwork

Programming Project Work In programming the technical work of the project, the project leader, together with the line engineer, determined the technical experiments to be done, using the technical proposal. The project leader then checked with the line engineer as to the technical feasibility of the experiments and as to how the experiments were related to the project's technical objectives. For experiments having comparable technical feasibility, the criterion used to select the experiment was, typically, the fewest number of man-hours.

Checking up on Work — Monthly Progress Reviews To plan the work and keep it moving along with minimum delay, the project leader held a network of informal meetings with project personnel, culminating in a formal meeting at the end of the month. In addition to dwelling on technical difficulties and proposed experiments, attention was focused on the task of planning future project activities within the limits of the budgeted man-hours. From the problems and delays uncovered in these meetings, the project leader developed the necessary corrective action to bring the technical work closer to the planned technical goals within the scheduled man-hour limits.

Implementing Management-Approved Project Changes Project changes usually came from management. Some of the typical changes were as follows:

1. Change in technical goals or related specification limits
2. Decision for cutoff or the continuance of some of the experiments
3. Shift in the priority rank of the project
4. Shift in the allocation of manpower

These changes were a form of corrective action that came about either as a result of the monthly progress reviews presented to management or as the result of requests from the project leader. In any event it was up to the project leader to make certain that technical changes (once approved by management) could be carried out within the limits of allocated manpower and time, and in addition, that the changes were understood by project personnel and were indeed carried out.

Promoting Project Teamwork Typically, in the companies studied, the project leader was not the organizational supervisor of project personnel. Management recognized the importance of a good working team, and they not only tried to assign a group of compatible line engineers to projects, but they also tried to honor the project leader's request for certain individuals. However, it was not always possible to have the ideal members available at the same time for assignment. The project leader therefore had to do his best in coordinating the efforts of his project team.

The only way the project leader could obtain preference as to the application of a line engineer's actual time to his project was through obtaining a higher priority for the project or getting permission from the respective functional heads.

Establishment of a high degree of cooperation among project personnel to encourage teamwork was of major concern to the project leader in the coordination of project activities. Via the monthly progress reviews the project leader attempted to maintain a smooth flow of information among the line engineers so that they became aware of how they could best serve their project colleagues, the project itself, and best implement their own progress.

The project leader's expediting of such services as blueprinting, purchasing of materials, and machine shop work, and his giving due recognition not only helped keep delays to a minimum but aided the project leader in his relationships with the line engineers. Faulty project coordination was always a threat to the working climate in the laboratory. The project leader typically recognized the importance of teamwork and of effectively handling line engineers.

Summary

The budget and the budgetary process in the companies participating in this study were useful to top management and the chief engineer in helping to set boundaries for laboratory work in line with the company's resources and market objectives, in allocating funds and deploying manpower over laboratory work, and in estimating if remaining funds were adequate to complete the project work. By comparing technical progress with the planned and expended amount of resources, the budget was also used as a device to control expenditures and to develop corrective action. In a general sense, the budget was used as a guide while evaluating the performance of the laboratory.

The project leader planned and conducted the project work within the limits of the budgeted engineering man-hours, and his ability to coordinate work and develop and execute corrective action influenced the project budget and budget changes. Changes involving the project work were translated into man-hour and timetable requirements by the project leader for management approval. The total laboratory output and performance was the grand sum of the work and results of the individual projects. Since project leaders coordinated the technical work, both individually and collectively, they were an important part of the management of the laboratory.

4
Standard Budgetary Process and the Role of the Project Leader

The objective of this chapter is to develop a typical budgetary process — that is, the process of developing and using the budget — and the role of the project leader in this process, synthesized from the procedures of the laboratories observed in this study. The purpose is to provide a basis for better understanding the project leader's role in budgeting and his use of the budget. In this chapter the chief engineer is considered the representative of top management, but at times he will be referred to individually for purposes of clarity. The typical, or standard, budgetary process, which was developed by extracting the practices common to two of the three laboratories, will be referred to as the "*Process*."

The Standard Budgetary Process

Development of the Process The Process consisted of the following three parts:

1. The total annual laboratory budget
2. The individual project budget
3. The monthly review for each of these budgets

The principal elements contained in each of the first two of these parts were formulation, approval, and administration of changes. According to the Process, the major elements of the monthly review consisted of expenditure and timetable analyses in the context of engineering work done. Responsibilities for parts of the Process were distributed among key positions in the organization as shown in Table 4-1.

Expense Budget — Capital Budget — Overhead Allocation In the Process, the total laboratory budget consisted of an expense budget and a capital budget. The total annual laboratory budget

TABLE 4-1

Distribution of Responsibility in Typical Budgetary Process

	Annual Laboratory Budget			Individual Project Budget		
	Higher Management	Top Management		Top Management		Project Leader
Element of Process		Division Manager	Chief Engineer	Division Manager	Chief Engineer	
Formulation		Joint effort		Joint effort		
Approval	Joint effort		Concurrence	Joint effort		Concurrence
Administration of changes	Joint effort		Concurrence	Joint effort		Concurrence
Monthly Progress Review						
Determination of technical progress			Prime responsibility			Prime responsibility
Expenditures related to technical progress		Joint effort			Prime responsibility	Partial responsibility[a]
Planning of work one month ahead					Concurrence	Prime responsibility
Adequacy of remaining resources		Joint effort			Prime responsibility	

[a] Man-hours versus technical progress analysis.

and the individual project budgets were essentially expense budgets containing noncapital items. The capital budget was a list of equipment and space needed over and above what was already on hand to perform the work of the laboratory. Expense items appearing on the budget included engineering labor, material, and overhead (out-of-pocket) charges. The total annual laboratory budget contained a list of all of these expenses showing the total yearly laboratory amount for each (Table 4-2). For monthly analysis, the typical total budget with its respective cost items were prorated over the calendar months of the fiscal year.

TABLE 4-2

TYPICAL TOTAL ANNUAL LABORATORY BUDGET

Item	Annual Amount budgeted (*in dollars*)
Staff personnel Engineering Technicians Drafting **TOTAL SALARIES**	
Overtime premiums Vacations and allowances **PAYROLL PREMIUMS**	
Social security Stock bonuses Other benefits **EMPLOYEE BENEFITS**	
Shop and office supplies Maintenance Blueprints Employee education Telephone and telegraph Travelling and entertainment Subcontract engineering Memberships and contributions Technical training programs Others **GENERAL OPERATING EXPENSES**	
Rental Insurance Depreciation **FIXED EXPENSES**	
General company assessments **ASSESSMENTS**	
TOTAL	

The individual project budget was reflected in terms of each of its direct expense items, such as engineering labor and material (Table 4-3). Overhead charges were not allocated on a project basis since effective control could not be exercised over overhead factors via project budgets. The project leaders individually did not have full control over the service groups, which comprised a large portion of the overhead charges. Hence there did not appear to be any benefit in allocating overhead costs to individual projects. Practice in the Process revealed that overhead charges could be more effectively controlled and managed in the laboratories by allocating them over the functional organizational units, such as the chemical engineering, electrical engineering, and other functional groups. The work load for these functional groups (a summation of their shares of work in each project) determined the size of each function in terms of number of engineers, facilities, and general operating expenses.

TABLE 4-3

INDIVIDUAL PROJECT BUDGET

Item	Budgeted amount (in dollars[a])
Engineering labor	
Technician labor	
Drafting labor	
Material	
Miscellaneous (Consulting, travel, etc.)	
TOTAL	

[a]Also available in man-hours.

Based on experience, each nonproject cost item of the total laboratory budget typically had correlation with the number of engineers. Hence, by estimating the total number of engineers required, it was possible to estimate the size of the overhead items for the laboratory. The number of engineers, therefore, was the only real connecting link between the individual project budgets and the overhead charges for the total laboratory.

The individual project budget was also used to estimate total material expenditures of the laboratory. Experience had also revealed that there was correlation between material expenses and direct engineering labor. Hence, based on the most recent correlation data, total material expenses were estimated either on a project-by-project basis or, directly, by estimation from the total laboratory engineering time.

As mentioned earlier, the individual project budget provided a means for estimating the laboratory capital budget. By converting the work requirements for each of the projects into net equipment and space needs over and above existing space and equipment, a total capital requirement was determined.

According to the Process, the formulation of the individual project budgets took place before the formulation of the total annual budget. The project selection system was such that the project budget was estimated as ideas for projects emerged during the year and not specifically during the annual-laboratory-budget preparation period.

Formulation Process for Individual Project Budgets Top management, with assistance from the chief engineer, formulated project budgets. The process used was as follows:

1. Top management established engineering objectives (project technical proposals).
2. Chief engineer translated objectives into technical problems and plans designed to yield their respective solutions.
3. Chief engineer translated engineering problems and solutions into cost factors — man-hours, materials, equipment, and space.
4. Chief engineer, with assistance from accounting data, converted cost factors into dollars.
5. Top management, with sales information (on desired com-

pletion date), estimated calendar time schedule per project and phased total project budget over calendar months.

Steps 1, 2, and 3 were expert estimates based on previous budgeting experience, technical knowledge, and engineering ability. The factor that linked and converted technical work to terms of budget was man-hours, the budgeted amounts varying directly with number of man-hours. Clearly, then, the man-hour estimate was the heart of the budget.

Step 4 was based on conversion factors developed from historical accounting data.

Step 5 was by and large the rate at which man-hours were allocated over calendar months, based on the plan of work and the desired completion date given by the sales department. The margin of error allowed was a factor developed from historical data of previous similar-type projects. It was impractical to estimate a standard margin of error because of the human element. Estimates varied with the people making them. Furthermore, the ability, knowledge, experience, and performance of a previous project team was not consistent with that of another project team. Therefore, the error computed from previous budgeted and actual project results was used only as a very general guide.

The final step of the typical process was to allocate direct project costs over the project calendar timetable. This projection was useful not only in computing the number of engineers needed and in reviewing the project at monthly intervals but also for estimating cash flow.

Formulation Process for Total Annual Laboratory Budget The major steps taken by top management in the Process — that is, the process for developing the total annual laboratory budget — were as follows:

1. Estimated total laboratory budget on a project-by-project basis.
2. Estimated total laboratory budget based on ratios developed from historical data by accounting (percent of estimated net profit, percent of estimated net sales).
3. Compared the different estimates for the total budget computed by (1) and (2) above.
4. From information above, developed order of magnitude of

total laboratory budget by reconciling difference between project-by-project estimate and estimate by ratios:
  a. Adjusted to make certain that enough funds from sales and profits (Step 2) covered work of all projects (Step 1);
  b. Adjusted to enable realistically acquiring additional engineers when needed.
5. Held preliminary meetings with higher management (level above division manager) to obtain their opinion as to what the order of magnitude of the total laboratory budget should be.

Management typically considered return on investment on a project-by-project basis as was described in Chapter 2 (Project selection). In the same chapter it was also pointed out that top management typically balanced return on investment against the need for a fuller line of products and against the firm's reputation and prestige in the market. The emphasis given by higher management and the division manager to some of the comparisons made was not known on the organizational level at which the study interviews were held. This information seemed difficult to obtain. The matter was not pursued further because this study was primarily concerned with the budgetary process as it took place at the levels of the chief engineer and the project leader.

Approval of Total Annual Laboratory Budget The next major step in the Process was the approval phase for the total annual laboratory budget. Before the budget was set forth for implementation, approval by higher management, which included the division manager and the level above him, was required. The approval function also included a kind of secondary approval at the chief engineer level. The chief engineers were allowed to rebut higher management's decision and to present any serious objections. Higher management realized that if the chief engineers were reluctant to accept the total budget, this fact could impair its successful implementation. The chief engineers, however, were primarily responsible for carrying out the budget requirements and taking steps to adhere to it. It was understood by both the chief engineer and higher management that the latter had the final "say-so." The typical attitude of the chief engineer was that in the final analysis it was higher management's responsibility to decide the total laboratory budget and that it was his job, even though he may not have agreed completely, to do his best to meet their wishes.

Approval of Individual Project Budgets Typically in the Process, final approval of the individual project budgets followed the approval of the total annual laboratory budget. If the final laboratory budget differed from the proposed annual laboratory budget, changes of a proportional nature were required of the individual project budgets. It followed that the total dollar budget for all individual project budgets could not exceed the total dollar size of the approved annual laboratory budget.

Approval of the individual project budgets rested with top management. Several major considerations were weighed in approving these budgets: first of all, if the total annual laboratory budget had been decreased in dollar size below the sum of the individual projects contemplated, the change necessarily confronted top management with the following alternatives:

1. To stretch out the timetable of one or more projects.
2. To defer or cancel project(s).

The criteria employed in deciding to stretch out a project depended on competition and customer demand and on the date the new product was needed. If there was no flexibility for "stretch-out," then management had to defer a project. If a competitor was involved, the criteria employed for stretch-out mainly depended on estimates of the competitor's date of completion. It was difficult for management to learn this kind of competitive information; however, sometimes customers would provide this information or clues, or sometimes a competitor's advertising program strongly hinted his completion date. If completion dates could not be adjusted, then management was again compelled to defer or drop a project. Before freezing the final project budgets, appropriate changes in the number of engineers needed and facilities required were made by top management. All of these considerations involved consultations with the chief engineer because he was responsible for carrying out the various projects in the laboratory. Typically, final approval of the individual project rested primarily with the division manager, and, secondarily, with the chief engineer. Although the chief engineer was responsible for getting the project work done, it remained the responsibility of the division manager to make the final approval decision.

Monthly Progress Reviews of Total Laboratory Budget and Individual Project Budgets It was general practice in the budgetary process to review the total annual laboratory budget every month. The review process involved the following steps:

1. Computation of a variance analysis report (usually by the accounting department, one for annual laboratory budget and one for each project), showing the arithmetic difference between the actual and budgeted cost
2. Determination of technical progress data by ascertaining technical accomplishments to date and matching them against the original plan of work
3. Relating of expenditures to technical progress
4. Making of financial projections, translating planned technical effort into dollars, time, and capital expenditures

In the typical monthly review process the division manager and the chief engineer each separately reviewed expenditures to date versus corresponding budgeted amounts for items appearing on the laboratory budget. The chief engineer felt that financial performance was in part a reflection on his ability to direct and manage the laboratory. In reporting progress he tried to anticipate the reactions and questions from the division manager. The cost variance on the laboratory budget items by themselves each pointed up the possibility of the following:

1. Arithmetic mistakes in computation
2. Faulty material expenditures
3. Faulty use of nonproject cost items

Management of the companies studied did not provide samples showing actual expenditures and corresponding variances because of the confidential nature of the information. As for variance on engineering labor charges, as long as overtime was not allowed and the manpower level fixed in accordance with the planned amount, such a variance seldom existed. The purpose of the variance report was to trace the deviations to their origins so that remedial action could be taken if necessary. However, the cost report for the laboratory as a whole did not show cost on a project basis (Table 4-4). Hence, the chief engineer received a project cost report from accounting showing the difference between actual and budgeted cost to date for engineering labor and material expenditures (Table 4-5). The variance computation for a project item by itself indicated the possibility of any one of the following:

TABLE 4-4

Monthly Operating-cost Report[a]
Total Laboratory

Item	Current month			Year to date		
	Actual	Budgeted	%[b]	Actual	Budgeted	%[b]
Staff personnel						
Engineering						
Technicians						
Drafting						
TOTAL SALARIES						
Overtime premiums						
Vacations and allowances						
PAYROLL PREMIUMS						
Social security						
Stock bonus						
Other benefits						
EMPLOYEE BENEFITS						
Shop and office supplies						
Maintenance						
Blueprints						
Employee education						
Telephone and telegraph						
Travelling and entertainment						
Subcontract engineering						
Memberships and contributions						
Technical training programs						
Others						
GENERAL OPERATING EXPENSE						
Rental						
Insurance						
Depreciation						
FIXED EXPENSES						
General company assessments						
ASSESSMENTS						
TOTAL						

[a] Prepared by accounting.

[b] Percent $= \dfrac{\text{Actual amount}}{\text{Budgeted amount}}$

TABLE 4-5

MONTHLY OPERATING-COST REPORT
PROJECT XYZ

Item	Current month	Year to date
Engineering Technicians Drafting Material Miscellaneous		
TOTAL		
Summary Budgeted amount Actual amount Percent[a]		

[a] $\text{Percent} = \dfrac{\text{Actual amount}}{\text{Budgeted amount}}$

1. Faulty estimating
2. Completion of work ahead of schedule leaving unexpended funds
3. Faulty use of allocated project resources (material and engineering man-hours)

The computed variance for a project item by itself was not very useful because it did not reveal the status of progress. Even a zero status did not mean that the work was on schedule with the budgeted cost and timetable amounts. Only by relating actual technical progress to planned progress was it possible to judge whether expenditures to date were commensurate with technical progress; this established a basis for corrective action. The project leader reported technical accomplishments to date and showed engineering work and problems still confronting the project. The essence of such reports will be described later in this chapter. To get a picture as to over-all project progress, the chief engineer compared the planned technical work in terms of expected technical mileposts and their corresponding budgeted man-hours, with actual technical accomplishments and their related expended man-hours to date. The chief engineer, in addition to his appraisal of progress, submitted what he considered pertinent technical information in his monthly report to the division manager, so that he, too, was equipped to relate variance and expenditures to date with technical progress and to devise corrective action if necessary. The technical progress information, prepared exclusively by the project leader and submitted in his monthly report, was an important part of the Process because it helped formulate the future direction of laboratory work. His engineering ability, experience from previous projects, and communication with project personnel played a large part in determining the information he reported.

The typical review process thus far described, related financial progress to technical progress but did not provide an answer to the question, Are remaining funds adequate to complete the laboratory's technical objectives in time? In order to do this, the Process called for relating remaining anticipated engineering work to unexpended funds. The chief engineer appraised the remaining technical work on a project-by-project basis using the project leader's monthly report and information gathered from his personal contact during the month with laboratory personnel. The chief engineer reported his findings to the division manager, along with recommendations showing an analysis of incremental funds needed to complete laboratory technical work. The division manager also conducted a similar analysis for the adequacy of the balance of funds for the work ahead and made his own general financial projection for the future work of the laboratory. These future projections did not necessarily change the original budget, especially if, in the opinion of top management, progress in future months was likely to catch up in such a manner as to eliminate any necessity for a change.

The budget was not worked out to reflect changes just to explore the financial implication of the changes and to obtain a new schedule of funds required, however. The purpose of the review was also to try to make certain that laboratory operations remained within scheduled financial and timetable limits. If a project was behind schedule, some of the kinds of corrective action that could be taken were the lowering of technical objectives, the cutting off of certain project experiments, the stopping of certain projects and the pushing ahead of others, or the acquisition of needed funds and time. Many of these considerations were discussed at informal meetings between the chief engineer and the division manager.

Administering Changes in Total Laboratory and Project Budgets

It was consistent with the budgetary concept to accept the fact that changes to the approved final budgets were inevitable and necessary for the successful conduct of laboratory activities. Management realized all too well that the laboratory work was of a dynamic nature and that budgets were no more accurate than the information on hand and the weakest link in the chain of supporting estimates.

Only changes in work load affecting the total manpower level of the laboratory brought about a change in the total laboratory budget. These changes typically resulted from adding a new project and/or pushing other projects ahead. The original final laboratory budget did not provide a "contingency" sum to account for unforeseen projects. Changes in the work load for individual projects did not always change total manpower levels because either the change in work was spread out over calendar time or the work of some projects was deferred, some projects being reduced in amounts that equalled the total increases in others.

The frequency of making revisions to the total laboratory budget depended on the need for additional work, the availability of funds, and the availability of the needed number of engineers. If an interim revision was contemplated for the annual laboratory budget, the method for estimating and making changes followed the same pattern as the formulation and approval steps of the Process. Higher management was responsible for approving changes to the total laboratory budget.

As project work progressed, more reliable information was available which provided a better basis for replanning the balance of the project work. During the early stages of a project, revisions were not generally made because of the uncertainty of the future work. However, as uncertainty decreased, significant changes, if necessary, were made to the project budget.

The project leader was permitted to exercise some discretion in making changes. These changes were resolved by the chief engineer only if they did not require more funds than the total amount provided for in the project budget. The chief engineer altered project budgets and timetables and technical objectives insofar as the over-all laboratory budget and goals were not altered.

The division manager had the final responsibility in approving changes to the total laboratory budget. If a significant change was contemplated concerning the remaining work of a project, the change was converted into budgetary and timetable terms and presented to top management for approval.

Changes usually emanated from two general sources: first, from influences outside the laboratory, and second, from the monthly budget reviews. Changes from the outside were brought about by changes in general economic conditions and in the specific market situation, that is, customer demand and competition. Types of changes coming from internal sources will be discussed later in this chapter when the role of the project leader in the monthly review process is described. It was imperative that changes be clearly defined and communicated to all people concerned; otherwise the technical and financial objectives for the laboratory were not understood and, consequently, not met. The periodic budget reviews not only provided a means for bringing changes about but also helped to communicate them.

Annual Period for Budget Preparation The process for developing the annual laboratory budget was a relatively long and meticulous task. In the companies studied, it started in August with a rough formulation of plans and ended in December with the development of the final total annual laboratory budget. The early plans were checked and rechecked and adjustments made as to the following:

1. Technical goals and feasibility of work
2. Agreement of estimated total budget with company resources
3. Ensuring of company's share of and position in the market

During this period, the Process typically had the chief engineer busy as much as several days per week working on the various aspects of the planning. The project leader was concerned only with the plans for the balance of his project, and when called upon, he was usually able to submit them within a week's time.

Typical Role of Project Leader in Budgetary Process

In the preceding discussion, the project leader was seen to have some responsibilities in the formulation of individual project budgets. In relation to "changes" in the project, his concurrence was sought but his complete approval was not mandatory. At best, management was satisfied with the promise of best effort. It was typical for the project leader to implement all changes relative to the project, most of which emanated from the periodic review phase of the typical budgetary process. In this phase the project leader's major responsibility was his appraisal of technical progress and the planning of work for the next month.

Typical Role in Budget Formulation During the annual budget preparation period, project budgets were prepared for in-process projects flowing into the next fiscal year and for any new projects being considered at the time. The project leader, however, did not participate in preparing new project budgets except in an indirect way. If the chief engineer knew beforehand which project leader was to be assigned to a particular project, then he had the project leader prepare the technical work plan, man-hours requirement, and the project timetable; but most of the time the project leader was not known at the time a new project budget was being formulated. The chief engineer took into account the performance characteristics of the company's typical project leader, based on previous performance in formulating project budgets. He was very careful to select project leaders by attempting to match the technical background and engineering ability of the man to the project, and further, by considering the project leader's ability to get along with people and to inspire project personnel to work together in a productive manner.

The project leader participated more actively in the replanning and budgeting of the in-process projects at the time of the annual budget preparation. The project leader typically did not submit a budget in dollars for his project but basically furnished man-hours requirements as a function of calendar time needed to finish his project. As has been stated before, the estimated man-hours requirement was the heart of the budget and was easily translated to dollars by using a conversion factor. The total man-hours estimate for the project was the sum of the individual estimates made by the line engineers with the help of the project leader. The final estimate at best was only as good as the men making them and was difficult to ascertain. The actual man-hours and timetable requirements for the average completed project was, typically, approximately 25 percent over the initial budgeted amounts. The error would have been greater if the technical goals had not been usually lowered as the projects drew near completion. Actual data showing budgeted man-hours versus actual man-hours was not made available because the information was considered confidential.

When a new project was assigned to a project leader, he did not replan the estimated man-hours and project timetable originally planned by management. The project leader felt that his estimate would be no more or less accurate than the original because of the inherent uncertainties in the technical work and because the technical goals were usually changed before completion.

Typical Role in Budget Approval The project leader's personal approval of his project's budget was not a typical requirement, but his concurrence was usually sought for best effort. He submitted man-hour and timetable data for his in-process project on the understanding that it was subject to change as management integrated individual projects into a total laboratory effort. These alterations were usually brought about essentially by a change in priority rank of projects for the fiscal year, by changes in market conditions, and by changes in resources allocated to other projects. The chief engineer valued the attitude and opinion of the project leader and sought his concurrence because the project's successful performance depended not only on the project leader's ability but on his desire for satisfaction and recognition of a job well done. Also, his point of view reflected those of the line engineers, hence adding to the importance of his concurrence.

Typical Role in Monthly Project-Progress Review The purpose of the monthly progress review from the project leader's point of view was to keep the project work moving along in accordance with the allocated man-hours and to try to complete the project in minimum time. The project leader reviewed the work of his project continually to check up on the engineering work activities, to help and make certain that experiments were getting done, and to better coordinate the interdisciplinary work. The monthly progress review meeting served as a means to communicate pertinent information from and among project personnel and to management. The essence of the project progress review and what was reported to management was as follows:

1. Determination of technical achievements to date
2. Comparison of progress made to date with technical achievements forecasted in original planning to help determine, with line engineers, if work was on schedule.
3. Planning of work (experiments to be tried, problems anticipated, methods of solution, expected results) for the next month with line engineers

The project leader's initial step was to review the variance cost report showing actual engineering labor and material costs versus the corresponding budgeted amounts. This was a check to make sure that only the allocated budgeted time was charged to his project, since line engineers typically worked simultaneously on other projects; and conversely, it also served as a check to see if allocated budgeted time (man-hours) was actually being charged. It was not enough to know that a variance existed, because it only showed the arithmetic difference between actual and budgeted time and allowed inferences as to status of progress; nor could any satisfaction be drawn from a report showing no variance.

Hence, the next step in the review process was the determination of technical progress to date. The purpose of this step was not only to carry variance analysis through to a meaningful point but also to know just what technical accomplishments had been achieved for the sake of using the experience to help determine and plan better what was yet to be done in the next month. The project leader had daily contact with individual line engineers to check the progress on major aspects of the work and its related difficulties. He was interested in expediting delays and avoiding them in the future in order to keep the interdisciplinary work coordinated and moving along.

The project leader then compared technical accomplishments to date with the original plan of work to see if technical progress was commensurate with expended engineering man-hours in order to better gauge and plan the amount of work projected into the next month within the range of budgeted man-hours. A lag in progress usually meant either that estimates of the original plan (amount of technical work versus man-hours over calendar time) were faulty, or that the project work encountered unforeseen delays, or that coordination was faulty.

In these monthly progress-review meetings the project leader, together with his line engineers, planned the experiments for the next month. They gave great emphasis to the evaluation of technical results and proposed experiments directed at the project's technical goals. In order to coordinate the interdisciplinary work of the project, the work of each of the line engineers was planned in terms of what needed to be done and who was responsible. The uncertainties of the technical work precluded the scheduling of line engineers' experiments as a function of calendar time. Every effort was taken by the project group to minimize the error in their decisions involving the technology of their work. They tried to select that experiment having comparable probability of technical success and taking the least number of man-

Typical Role of Project Leader in Budgetary Process 53

hours so that their general line of action minimized total cost and time. On controversial issues, based on the judgment of the project leader, the chief engineer was consulted for his comments and instruction.

Up to this point in the progress review there was no attempt to look ahead towards the final completion of the project. If a project was less than halfway completed in terms of calendar time and technical achievements, it was typical of the project leader not to replan and establish a timetable for the balance of the budgeted man-hours. They argued that the net effect on the project's time schedule and remaining man-hours would in all probability be changed by the solution of problems still ahead of the project, thereby rendering any early re-estimates no more or less accurate than the original. If at the early stage of a project a major technical problem arose, however, then the entire project and the plan for its conduct was re-evaluated.

If the project was nearing completion at a point more than halfway through, then attention was given to calendar time and to remaining man-hours in the context of remaining technical work. If the completion date was rigorously tied to a predetermined factory schedule, a sales promotion plan, and/or a customer promise, the timetable re-evaluation was very thorough. In looking ahead, the question, Can the project be completed within the unexpended engineering man-hours and within the remaining calendar time? was not asked by the project leader during the early stages of the project. And, as pointed out above, since concern grew only as the project neared its final stages, it was then that he gave greater emphasis to the resources and calendar time available.

Typical Role in Budget Changes Any kind of change relative to project work usually had some effect on its budget. These changes came from the chief engineer for direct implementation. Those coming from the project leader and the line engineers that affected the project's technical goals, timetable, man-hours, and material and equipment needs were put into effect only after they were approved by the chief engineer. On the other hand, however, changes relative to experimental design, further experimentation, and reduced material and equipment needs were sanctioned by the project leader without additional approval so long as the project technical goals, budget, and timetable were not adversely affected.

The project leader was responsible for making sure that all changes were carried out. This involved translating changes into work plans and specific assignments for line engineers. Most important to the project leader was a meticulous translation of changes into technical problems and related methods of solution in order to develop meaningful assignments. A poor and unclear technical assignment not only reflected adversely on the project leader's performance but it retarded technical progress and in all probability increased the project's total cost.

Summary

According to the typical budgetary process, the estimated man-hours requirement was the heart of the budget. The initial estimates on man-hours for the project budget were made by top management and not by the project leader because usually he was not known at the time these estimates were made. When the project leader was assigned a project, he did not replan and make an estimate of his own on man-hours and calendar time needed for his project. Only if his in-process project carried over into the next fiscal year did he provide man-hour estimates and calendar time projections to the chief engineer. The work planned ahead by project personnel was programmed within budgeted man-hour limits, and the estimates were no better than the men making them. The over-all margin of error on a typical project averaged about 25 percent on the "over" rather than the "short" side, and would have been greater had not technical goals usually been adjusted downward.

▶▶▶▶ **5**

Limitations to Project Leader's Use of Budgets

In this chapter the typical limitations besetting the project leader in the budgetary process are briefly described and their relationships to the budgetary process indicated. The purpose is to provide a basis for better understanding the project leader's problem in the use of the budget as a management tool.

The various limitations are discussed according to the following breakdown:

1. Limitations as seen by the project leader
2. Limitations as seen by the chief engineer
3. Limitations as seen by the author

The list of major limitations was gathered through personal interviews with the chief engineer and three project leaders in each of the three companies. Although the problems as seen by the project leader, the chief engineer, and the author are different (Table 5-1), it did not necessarily mean that they did not concur with one another. During the interviews the respondents were inclined to reflect what they felt were the most important impediments.

The subject matter of the information gathered was mostly subjective. When discussing a particular phenomenon or limitation, the respondents described the difficulties they encountered and how the difficulties came about, but they did not generally illustrate their points with quantitative material on the grounds that the information was confidential, and that some of it might reflect adversely on the company's ability. For example, in discussing the effects of planning and scheduling limitations, the respondents would not even present data showing orders of magnitude of faulty performance in terms of time and cost.

Limitations as Seen by Project Leader

The following is a list of typical limitations that confronted the project leader:

1. Vague technical specifications
2. Low predictability
3. Lack of a workable scheduling device
4. Little authority over line engineers
5. Thinly spread manpower

The frequency of occurrence of these limitations among those interviewed is shown in Table 5-1.

Vague Technical Specifications In two of the reporting companies the technical goals (specifications) were sometimes stated vaguely, as illustrated by the following examples:

1. Frequency — "up to 1000 megacycles"
2. Frequency — "range 800 to 1000 megacycles"

Stating the specification in these ways was puzzling to the project leader. To illustrate, the general experimental design and the engineering calculations (chemical, electrical, and mechanical) were usually the same in principle for different values of frequency, but each value of frequency required its own set of experimental "runs" and each needed a set of engineering calculations. Usually when specifications were quoted vaguely, the project engineers selected not one but several arbitrary values (for example, 800, 900, and 1000 megacycles) and experiments were put under way for solution until one of the desired values was successfully reached.

In contrast, if a fixed specification goal for frequency had been set, there would not have been need for the project leader to fix several arbitrary frequency values, and therefore only one set of engineering calculations would have been made. Vague specifications, according to the project leaders, tended to increase the work load and make the planning more complex.

Top management justified its stand on two points. First of all, it felt that high goals were an incentive to engineers and that traditionally, actual end results were always something less than what had been aspired to. Secondly, top management usually did not know what specification limits a competitor might set for his new product, and at other times, top management did not know the exact technical

TABLE 5-1
LIMITATIONS FACED BY THE PROJECT LEADER

Limitation	Number of Companies of 3 Reporting	Number of Project Leaders of 9 Reporting	General source of limitation
A. Limitations as Seen by the Project Leader			
Vagueness of some project technical specifications	2	6	Management
Low predictability	3	9	State of scientific creative process
Lack of workable scheduling device	3	9	Cannot measure input factors of scientific creative process
Lack of organizational authority over line engineers	3	9	Organization
Manpower spread too thin	3	9	Low predictability; shortage of engineers
B. Limitations as Seen by the Chief Engineer			
Lack of effective planning	3	Majority	Project leader (lack of administrative and technical know-how)
C. Limitations as Seen by the Author			
Line engineers' lack of understanding of budgeting	3	9	Lack of background and training
Project leader's lack of understanding and know-how in use of budget	3	8	Lack of background and training
Poor communications among project personnel	3	9	Lack of technical and administrative know-how

limits for the end use of the product; hence, management refrained from freezing specifications too early in order to equal or better a competitor's product or until end use characteristics were known. In the minds of the engineers there was a marked difference between a frozen specification and one set as a goal. The frozen specifications meant that they had reached a point of no change, the goal that there was still flexibility relative to change. The latter instance, in the minds of the engineers, had a greater element of uncertainty, which tended to complicate their planning.

The technical specifications of a project were related to the project leader's use of the budget. Since vague specifications (and the element of uncertainty) precluded spelling out clearly what had to be done, the project leader's planning in order to coordinate project work within budgeted man-hour limits became proportionately less effective, and his estimates of man-hours and timetable requirements for project work were less accurate.

Low Predictability The project leader typically used the term *low predictability* to refer to the uncertainty in forecasting technical problems, its methods of solution, and the probabilities of success. The project leader felt that the element of low predictability was the most important problem facing him in the budgetary process. Hardly any phase of the project was conducive to accurate forecasting. Estimates for such factors as manpower, cost, completion date, and ability to meet technical objectives were all very subjective in nature. The experience and ability of the technical personnel involved were the controlling factors in guiding these judgment-type decisions.

In forecasting a project budget, the translation of major technical problems into technical work assignments was one of the most important steps because an error at this point manifested itself in the many phases of the developed project budget, affecting manpower requirements, costs, and time schedules.

In setting up the technical work problems, the determination of alternative problems was first made. The most appropriate alternatives were then selected according to both technical and economic feasibility. The next major step involved the selection of the most appropriate method of solution, again as to technical and economic feasibility. Even if accurate decisions concerning the selection of appropriate problems and of methods of solution were made, there still remained the task of forecasting how many runs, or cycles of experiments, would be necessary to achieve successful completion.

From the foregoing it is apparent, as stated by project leaders, that the laboratory history of similar-type technical work and the technical ability of project personnel helped in partially mitigating the element of uncertainty, because usually better (or more astute) scientific know-how tended to reduce the chance of technological error.

Low predictability was related to the project leader's use of the budget because the element of uncertainty made his planning, scheduling, and coordinating ineffective. His attempt to work within budgeted man-hours and timetable limits was proportionally ineffective. Then, too, his man-hour and timetable estimates were less accurate. The knowledge that predictability was low caused project personnel to resist budgeting, and this resistance added to the ineffectiveness of the budgetary process.

Lack of Workable Scheduling Device The project leader typically felt the need for a workable scheduling device because he was responsible for coordinating the complex of interdisciplinary effort that comprised the project's activities. He needed to know when work had to be done in order to better dovetail project activities and to help line engineers arrange the timing of their experiments, because their work was interrelated with the work of other line engineers. The project leader also felt that a workable scheduling device would help him in the management of the appropriate timing of services, material needs, and facilities to the awaiting technical work assignments.

There was a general lack of an effective scheduling device, however, and this lack was related to budgeting at the project level. Without scheduling it was not possible to allocate funds (man-hours) accurately over the life of a project against calendar time. Poor scheduling caused delays, increasing costs and making the project budget inaccurate and difficult for the project leader to adhere to. Moreover, with poor scheduling, any project leader man-hour estimates for future work were less realistic.

Little Authority over Line Engineers The project leader typically complained of his weak or nonexistent authority over line engineers. The line engineer was assigned to a project but reported administratively to the functional head of his group and not to the project leader. As a result, the line engineer's technical work was usually directed more by the functional group head, who was typically a senior scientist specializing in the area of his function, rather than by the project leader. Under these conditions the project leader depended on the contributions of each of the line engineers to navigate the project work through the various disciplinary functional areas. In this maze the project leader encountered numerous impediments, some of which are listed below:

1. The project leader gave and could give only little technical assistance because line engineers were of different scientific disciplines, in most of which the project leader lacked training.
2. The project leader could not direct and schedule the day-to-day work load of line engineers; instead, the respective functional heads, together with the line engineers, were responsible.
3. In part, the line engineers were motivated by their own interests in deciding when to work on a project, and their decisions at times conflicted with project interests.
4. The project leaders frequently found themselves competing with one another for the time and services of the line engineers.

Under the above conditions, the project leader could have sought chief engineer assistance to expedite work. But the project leader usually did not want to go over the heads of his line engineers and their functional heads for fear of alienating them.

The lack of real authority over line engineers was related to the project leader's role in the budgetary process. The fact that the project leader did not deploy the line engineer's time made his dovetailing of work difficult and inaccurate. It also precluded the project leader from getting work done within budgeted man-hour limits and from making appropriate timely cutoff on questionable experimentation. Therefore, the poor scheduling of project work made project budgeting proportionally inaccurate.

Thinly Spread Manpower The project leader typically observed that line engineers were "spread too thin." On the average, line engineers were assigned simultaneously to two projects each and sometimes three. The project leader invariably claimed that the project work assignments frequently awaited the attention of the line engineers.

The project leader argued that a multiproject work load like this helped dissipate the energy and effort of the line engineers and prevented them from concentrating long enough on difficult work assignments. He claimed that the line engineers' switching back and forth among as many as three projects in one month prevented them from devoting a steady stream of concentrated effort. Every switch was time consuming and hence tended to delay project work. In addition, because line engineers were assigned to several projects, project work usually awaited his attention, and hence the elapsed time for each phase was of necessity spread out; this increased the opportunity for delay.

On the other hand, the unpredictable problems inherent in a project were not usually the only ones delaying it. The major reasons for delay usually lay with other factors. There were intermittent interruptions from crash programs of other projects and sometimes from special laboratory investigations concerning problems of factory production items. The opportunity for the "bumping" process to occur increased the more a project was spread out over calendar time. The percentage of total time lost due to bumping was not significantly different providing each project had its share of equal opportunity to bump.

Limitations of Project Leader as Seen by Chief Engineer

The work of the laboratory typically fell under the jurisdiction of the chief engineer. He was the man whom top management held responsible. As is true in most cases, in these three companies each chief engineer had once been a project leader. Therefore, it seemed reasonable to conclude that the chief engineer's opinions about project leaders should be determined and should be given careful thought. It was interesting to learn that the chief engineers were almost of one mind in judging the main limitation besetting the project leader in the budgetary process. They felt that while low predictability was a chief problem, its roots were deeply imbedded in the nature of research and development engineering. On what they considered to be a more practical level — that is, something that might be more controllable — the main limitation was that typically the project leader did not plan thoroughly enough.

More and Meaningful Planning The chief engineers felt that the need for more and meaningful planning was a major deficiency of the project leader. By this they meant that work to be done was not always anticipated in time to give sufficient consideration to all of the factors it would be desirable to explore, allowing enough leeway to make opportune considerations.

Planning generally started with the project technical proposal, which was broad in scope and defined only the major objectives. The chief engineers admitted that the technical proposal as an over-all plan was not detailed enough for the project leader in organizing the day to day technical assignments. Many of the broader problems embraced a series of subproblems, the individual completion of which brought about the solution of the broader problem. Then, too, the project leader had to set up the sequence of problem solutions because of the interrelatedness of the project work.

The interdisciplinary nature and the multitude of experiments presented the project leader with the chance for overlooking and forgetting material and other service requirements. Even the assistance of the line engineers, who were familiar with the technical area and who helped with the planning, did not reduce the need for more planning. Moreover, one chief engineer stated that more of the experiments could have been performed simultaneously, as against the tendency for conducting them in tandem. Another of the chief engineers cited instances when the need for material, tools, and test equipment had been overlooked until the actual need for them had arisen. In this latter instance, the chief engineer did not think that the project leader could not do it, or would not do it, or that it was impossible to do, but, rather, ascribed it to faulty planning. The project leader typically spent a substantial portion of his time planning the coordination of the project activities. The project leader checked the work to be done by the line engineer, who was primarily responsible for planning and performing the work. A large portion of the technical work was not of the basic or applied research type ("blue sky") but was development-type engineering, where the technical work required could be spelled out more clearly.

Lack of effective planning at the project level was related to the project leader's use of the budget. In order to estimate the budget, usually the project needed to be dissected into smaller problems so that a more accurate estimate of engineering time, material, and facility requirements could be made. Good planning was therefore necessary for good budgeting. Unanticipated work made the budget estimate less accurate because the needed engineering man-hours and material were not included. In addition, untimely acquisition of material and facilities created delays, consuming valuable engineering time and tending to decrease the budget accuracy.

Limitations of Project Leader as Seen by Author

Based on his own observations of what seemed to be happening in these three companies, it became apparent to the author that the project leader was faced with three other important limitations:

1. Line engineers' lack of understanding of budgeting
2. Project leader's lack of know-how and understanding of how budgets could be used
3. Faulty communications among project personnel

Line Engineers' Lack of Understanding of Budgeting Each of the chief engineers claimed that frequently project work assignments (experiments) continued when they should have been stopped, because of the line engineer's basic desire for technical success. The companies were fearful of disclosing an actual example of cutoff showing the frequency and the order of magnitude of "excess" time spent, even on a disguised basis. Top management felt that such disclosure might be a damaging reflection on their ability to manage cutoff, a matter which they considered confidential. However, they did reveal the criteria for making cutoff decisions, which were described in Chapter 3. In the chief engineer's opinion cutoff was discouraged and further experimentation was spurred on, by and large, by either of two major conditions: the challenge of probable failure to the line engineer, or the probability that success was close at hand.

Because the line engineer was motivated by strong personal interest, he could have easily rationalized his technical victory as a gain also to the company. Based on interviews with project leaders, the line engineer was not usually trained in, or experienced with, or aware of budgetary matters and their concept. Late cutoff appeared, at least, to be partial evidence of the line engineer's lack of awareness of project-budget limits and the significance of the budget. It was more likely that late cutoff was an indication of his lack of understanding as to how engineering work and his technical objectives fit into the supply of laboratory resources budgeted to his project, rather than being a deliberate extended misuse of company funds.

Cutoff was vitally related to the project leader's use of the budget, since tardy cutoff decisions consumed valuable and costly engineering time and made scheduling ineffective because of the delay created.

Project Leader's Lack of Understanding of How Budgets Could Be

Used The chief engineers pointed out that the project leaders generally did not understand budgeting, a claim that was further substantiated by the typical project leader's own admission of his lack of understanding. On the basis of the typical project leader's role in the monthly review process, he did not fully use budget and schedule data. During the monthly review meeting, the typical project leader ascertained and reported technical progress and planned the work for the following month (Table 5-2).

TABLE 5-2

MONTHLY PROJECT-PROGRESS REVIEW PROCESS

Areas of Consideration	Items Reported
I. Work completed this month	Description of completed work

II. Work in process
  A. Previous work not completed
 	
  B. Work started during month
	1. Technical difficulties encountered and other delays
	
	2. New approach and/or remedy
	  a. Technical feasibility
	  b. Contribution to project technical goals
	  c. Anticipated delays (materials, manpower, facilities)
	  d. When and by whom it will be done

III. Work to be started next month	See (2) above

Although extended cutoff points for experiments were partly encouraged by personal motivations, the project leaders admitted that they did not consider such experiments in the context of remaining economic resources for the project (man-hours and calendar time). Moreover, the project leader had a master technical program consisting of major technical objectives, which he always evaluated and adjusted in the light of accumulated technical results so as to keep results in line with objectives. But, by his own admission, the project leader did not regularly during the monthly review period evaluate the balance of project work in the context of remaining project funds (man-hours) and calendar time.

The typical project leader did not gauge the cost (man-hours) of any particular experiment as being out of line with the project budget. However, based on his intuition, if a cost appeared high, it was reported to the chief engineer, who, as the representative of management, was responsible for the project budget. There were some project leaders who felt that in time a high cost trend would be noticed by comparing total actual cost with estimated total project cost. However, this comparison was performed too late after the fact to effectively cope with this kind of adverse cost variation. A large volume of this type of variation was practically uncontrollable.

The project leader's lack of know-how and understanding of the use of budgets tended to bring about the following:

1. Poor cutoff decisions on experimentation
2. Delayed corrective action

In addition, the project leader missed opportunities to bring the project to completion within the budgeted man-hour and timetable limits and so tended to defeat the "control" purpose of budgeting, especially when many work decisions were made at the project level independent of the chief engineer.

Faulty Communications among Project Personnel Faulty communications existed between the project leader and the line engineers, and between the project leader and the chief engineer. Timely flow of information among project personnel did not exist, and in addition, the chief engineer was very often likely to receive biased and censored reports on technical progress. The extent to which some of the project work assignments penetrated into the various disciplinary areas was sometimes beyond the general knowledge of the project leader. This lack of full understanding also prevailed among line engineers of different disciplines. The difficulty in understanding some of the profound technical issues of one another's work not only tended to inhibit the timely flow of, but very likely caused a distortion in, the information communicated. According to the project leaders, line engineers were usually too burdened with assignments to take time always to enlighten the project leaders. Eventually the important information emerged from periodic conferences, but only after the passing of valuable time.

The faulty flow of information to the project leader and then to the chief engineer also related to the matter of poor cutoff performance on experiments. Line engineers generally tended to prevent early cutoff on their experiments because of their personal and vested interests, which encouraged them to bias and censor their progress reports. And they were able to do so partly because project leaders were often poorly informed on relevant technical problems.

Faulty communications were again related to the project leader's use of the budget. For the reasons just noted, the project leader often found it difficult to communicate sufficiently for his own edification, and this inadequate flow of information in turn weakened planning and scheduling and made the project budget less effective.

Summary

In the companies visited, several major limitations confronting the project leader inhibited his use of the budget and restricted its usefulness when he did utilize it. Limitations like low predictability (which was malignant throughout every phase of project work), a need for better planning and scheduling, lack of project leader's real authority over line engineers, faulty progress reviews, and poor communications emerged as impediments hampering the project leader in his use of budgeting as a management tool.

Because of the difficulties typically cited by the project leader, it is unlikely that budgeting can be a useful management tool for the project leader unless the underlying conditions relative to the difficulties are changed.

▶▶▶▶ **6**

Low Predictability

Increased knowledge about low predictability will enable the reader to better understand the project leader's use of the budget. The purpose of this chapter is to demonstrate the prevalence of low predictability in the budgetary process at the project level in the three companies investigated and to explain how and why low predictability arose.

Low predictability, as described in the preceding chapter, was malignant in nature — its tentacles stretched out into every facet of the laboratory's work. The administrative and technical processes were not only continually threatened but complicated and retarded. Because of the poor ability to forecast, top management found it difficult to determine the size, shape, and direction of the company R & D program, the chief engineer found it equally difficult to manage R & D within the limits set by top management, and the project leader was confronted with a proportionate amount of difficulty in directing his project to a reasonable conclusion.

Low Predictability and Uncertainty

Each of the three chief engineers stated that the degree and accuracy of prediction depended, by and large, on how much of the science was known concerning the technical problems of his projects. One chief engineer pointed out that in the beginning not enough was known about the answers being searched for to make it possible to predict with reasonable accuracy what and when regarding technical results, but as project work progressed, more information became available and tended to improve predictability.

Uncertainty in Forecasting Process for Budget

In the previous chapters the general forecasting process for the budget as typically employed by the project leader was described. Some of the main elements are listed below:

1. Determination of technical problems to be solved
2. Determination of technical methods for solution of problems
3. Determination of technical feasibility
4. Determination of number of experimental trials, or runs, to reach conclusion
5. Estimation of the number of man-hours needed
6. Translation of man-hours into elapsed time requirements (involved acquisition of schedule data from such services as purchasing and machine shop)
7. Translation of manpower, material, and facility requirements into budget amounts (formulation of budgets by project leader not common)

A major portion of the uncertainty in R & D work stemmed from the interpretation of known theory and its application through experimental methods to bring about the desired technical results. Empirically in the planning process, each of the project problems and related methods of solution had to be identified, defined, and quantitatively measured in terms of man-hours and calendar time in order to achieve a high level of predictability. But there were many impediments under the existing conditions and under the prevailing state of the art of R & D administration.

Forecasting Information Based on "Guesses" In estimating forecasts for in-process projects, much of the information came from those line engineers who were responsible for performing the work. Because no better method was known, a good portion of the gathered forecasting information and data was based on expert "guesses." The actual accuracy of these guesses was difficult to ascertain, and to a large degree, they depended upon the experience and technical ability of the line engineer and project leader. The guessing involved not only the definition of problems to be solved and their related methods of solution but also the conversion of the planned work into man-hours and calendar time requirements. The chief engineers in the three companies reporting pointed to the preponderance of guessing, and according to them, there was no real alternative because part of the planning information needed was the object of the experiments being planned.

In addition to reliable expert guesses, good planning depended on the free and timely flow of complete information among project personnel, the project leader, and management. The communication process will be more fully discussed in Chapter 8.

Forecasting in Production versus Forecasting in R & D

Forecasting per se has commonly been a part of the budgetary process for the marketing, financial, and manufacturing branches of industrial firms. By comparing the scheme for forecasting production with that for forecasting laboratory output, it is possible to discern the significance of low predictability that prevails in R & D.

In production, output can be controlled by controlling input; that is to say, a combination of appropriate kinds and quantities of material and equipment, together with an appropriate number of people properly directed, usually renders a desired production output. In production there are shortages in capacity due to factors like absenteeism, machine breakdowns, rush orders, reworks, and material shortages, the magnitudes of which can be estimated from historical data and applied in forecasting capacity. In R & D the sources for capacity shortages are generally similar, but their estimates are less accurate because of the greater uncertainty in R & D work.

The production process is not always, but is usually, broken down into individual operations developed from a carefully prepared scientific specification. The exact kind and amount of input materials, along with the exact type of needed equipment per production unit, usually can also be scientifically determined from the blueprint and process specification. There is not much difference in the general way of planning the manpower, material, and equipment in R & D once the steps of the project have been laid out. In production, estimates for manpower requirements, related rates of production, and capacity rates for equipment have a higher degree of certainty than in R & D because production input data are more definable, available, measurable, and controllable. A comparison of the production of a new product in a plant for the first time, with an R & D project illustrates the difference in the degree of uncertainty.

The material need (type and amount) on a per product basis is usually determined from the blueprint of the new product. Not having actual production experience for the new product, the efficiency of material usage is estimated with "some error" from actual previous experience on similar production and the judgment of production engineers. First the rate of output of equipment and labor is usually estimated, with some error, by extrapolating productivity data from fundamental work operations of a similar, older production item. The estimated material usage and production rates usually can be estimated fairly accurately depending on the degree of correlation with previous similar production experience on the basis of measured fundamental work operations common to both the new product and older production. The products representing the older production do not need to be similar as to geometry or type as long as the fundamental work motions and methods are similar. In production, motion-time-method (MTM) analysis makes it possible to transfer past experience to a new product with fairly reliable accuracy.

In contrast, the input factors of R & D such as the creative ability of manpower and the needed knowledge, are not relatively as easily discernible. It is not possible to have a complete set of pertinent technological information. As a matter of fact, these data are an integral part of the total research and development objective. There is no "blueprint" in R & D. The existing theory and known experimental practices are combined in the best way possible when planning material and work effects. Although it is possible to predetermine the kinds of scientific disciplines needed, the exact number of personnel and their respective rates of creativity are expert "guesses" not determinable as accurately as in production. Previous experience in the laboratory is transferable but not, however, as easily, because of the lack of a technique such as MTM. The difficulty in extrapolating previous experience can be ascribed to the nature and character of the creative process, which comprises such less measurable items as experience and ability, basic knowledge, imagination, and working climate. From the foregoing comparison it is clear that the fundamental planning approaches appear to be similar, except that in R & D the degree of uncertainty is much greater.

The process of judging the creative productivity of an engineer is difficult and very subjective. John E. Arnold, of Stanford University, has related mental blocks, of both perceptual and emotional origin, to creativity.[1] Some of the perceptual blocks described by Arnold per-

[1] Charles S. Whiting, *Creative Thinking*, New York: Rheinhold Publishing Corporation, 1958, p. 12.

tain to isolating the problem, narrowing the problem, seeing remote relationships, and distinguishing between cause and effect.[2] Arnold has described some of the emotional blocks as fear of making a mistake, pathological desire for security, fear of supervisors, and distrust of colleagues and subordinates.[3] Knowing some of the difficulties involved in attempting to understand the creative process, the chief engineers interviewed nevertheless felt that they were able to rank project leaders and line engineers according to ability based on their judgment of the engineers' past performances. However, because of the personal nature of such a ranking, they refused to disclose this kind of information except to state that their primary criterion was how well the engineer had met his technical objectives in past projects.

Summary

Forecasting of production and R & D work was generally the same in principle; however, there appeared to be more uncertainty in R & D. The standards for predicting in R & D were very subjective and difficult to define, and the accuracy of the predictions was indeterminable. The foundation of R & D budgets was "guesswork" with wide and unknown limits of error and to a major degree, the error was intrinsic and unchangeable. Because of the uncertainty involved, low predictability was a vital factor in the project leader's suspicion of budgeting. Predictability improved as project work progressed, and by and large, the limits of error in forecast depended on the technical abilities and judgment of those doing the work.

[2] *Ibid.*
[3] *Ibid.*, p. 15.

7
Planning and Scheduling in the Context of Low Predictability

The purpose of this chapter is to show evidence pointing to the need for more effective planning and scheduling at the project level. Some of the major implications of the difficulties in planning and scheduling of concern to the project leader in the budgetary process and to management will be discussed.

The word planning means many things to many people. Implicit in its meaning is the preparation required to develop and design what is needed to carry a program to its successful conclusion. Usually the responsibility for planning carries with it the hazards of uncertainty, including unwanted acts of commission as well as those of omission.

It might be asked, How perfect can planning be? The answer depends considerably on the nature and character of what is being planned, the experience and ability of those planning, and the order of magnitude of the related disposable resources.

According to the budgetary process in the three companies reporting, the over-all laboratory budget, which was formulated by the chief engineer and top management, was based on the integrated activities of each of the active projects. Individual project programs combined became the total activity covered by the laboratory budget. As each project was fitted into the scope of the laboratory's total budget, it was often adjusted accordingly. Therefore, in reality, the total laboratory budget reflected the technical objectives, manpower, and facility requirements of each project. The budgetary process was a planning tool for the chief engineer and top management to help them program the activities of the laboratory. According to the typical chief engineer, budgeting helped keep the R & D activity in line with company objectives and resources.

Project Leader's Need for More Effective Planning

Chief Engineer's Definition of Effective Planning Project leader planning as explained by each of the chief engineers included the following:

1. Determining what has to be done
2. Working items in (1) above into a workable program
3. Handling people effectively
4. Avoiding costly delays and endeavours

The project leader was typically in general concurrence with the chief engineer's opinion that a project leader was not entirely stripped of planning responsibilities. Each project leader pointed out that his planning was a joint effort accomplished primarily in conjunction with and through the line engineers.

The typical project leader needed to do more effective planning, according to the chief engineers, who felt it was feasible and practical though difficult for a project leader to do a better job of planning. The difficulties, they believed, were inherent in the very factors causing the need for better planning, namely:

1. Low predictability
2. Project technical proposal too broad
3. Lack of full exchange of technical information between disciplines related to project work
4. Need for better handling of project personnel
5. Late cutoff point on project experiments

Each of the chief engineers of this study were in agreement as to the relevance of the above-listed factors to the need for more effective planning. They all agreed that the project leader could have done little to improve predictability, but as for technical matters, they felt that the project leader could have minimized some of the uncertainty in planning by building up his technical "know-how." In relation to Item 2, they realized also that some of the technological problems of the project were not defined or fully described at the outset, and while this was not the project leader's responsibility, the lack of clarity was a hindrance to him. The chief engineers also believed that project planning would have been generally improved and more effective if the project leader had developed more skill in handling people; and effective planning would have been a definite aid in coordinating project personnel.

Factors Contributing to Ineffective Planning The element of low predictability and factors contributing to it were described in the preceding chapter. In this section some of the same factors will be discussed but with more specific reference to planning project work.

Vague specifications. As pointed out in Chapter 5, management sometimes set technical goals high and specified them in a vague way. Vague specifications compelled project personnel to undergo additional sets of experimentation and engineering calculations. For example, in trying to plan work with a vague specification reading, "Attain up to 1000 megacycles in frequency," the planning of several groups of successive experiments was usually involved. Briefly, an arbitrary value thought to be reasonably attainable, say 700 megacycles, was set up first as an experimental goal. If the first round of experimentation was successful at 700 megacycles, then successive rounds of experiments at progressively higher frequency values were staged until 1000 megacycles was attained. If achievement was short of 1000 megacycles, the highest value reached was the one submitted to management as the feasible frequency goal. On the other hand, if the first experiments failed to achieve 700 megacycles, the project leader generally reversed his direction (700 downward) until he was able to achieve a frequency value successfully. During such a trial-and-error process the project leader tended to consult management at short intervals as to the acceptability of frequency values successfully reached up to that point in time. In contrast, had management rigidly set the frequency requirement at 1000 megacycles and not specified the possibility of accepting a lower value, the experimental work would have been gauged to, and the related engineering calculations based on, 1000 megacycles for the initial goal, and after several trials, if unsuccessful, the results would have been reported to management.

The project leaders interviewed (along with the line engineers) objected to the principle of setting high approximate limits for technical specifications. They felt that it increased the complex of experiments and added to the planning work load. The project leaders also felt that under "vague specifications" conditions they were precluded from making regular, on-the-job decisions and were therefore compelled too frequently to seek top management sanction to see if the attained achievements (results short of the goal) were acceptable.

Low Predictability. Each chief engineer recognized that his project leaders were handicapped by the prevalence of low predictability. In determining what had to be done in terms of technical day-to-day work assignments, the project leaders' only official program was the project technical proposal. The chief engineers stated that the project proposals were too broad to be used directly in planning and developing daily work assignments. According to the forecasting scheme used in the typical budgetary process, the complex of daily work assignments did not come directly from the project technical proposal but from an intermediate step consisting of subproject problems. The work was then arranged in proper sequence and chronological order for implementation. According to the chief engineers, the error in planning tended to increase as technical work assignments were programmed too far into the future, because of the uncertainty in predicting technical results that were needed to plan ensuing experiments.

The chief engineers ascribed the difficulty in planning mainly to the element of low predictability which, in part, developed from the inability of project leaders to determine and measure the input parameters of the creative process, such as technical knowledge needed, use of technical knowledge by project personnel, and the productivity of the project personnel.

Faulty Communications. The regular monthly planning process depended on the smooth flow of pertinent technical information among project personnel. The chief engineers typically felt that the project leader had difficulty in extracting information from line engineers, a factor tending to retard the efficiency of project planning. For example, the monthly planning of project work for the next successive monthly period depended on the evaluation of what had already been done, which was by and large based on the exchange of information among project personnel. This was somewhat unlike production, where performance was more conducive to measurement, for example, counting output and inspecting quality in tangible terms. The project leader's typical difficulties in communicating technical information to project personnel will be covered more fully in Chapter 9.

In R & D, "information" was by and large the item being produced, and therefore, in the normal process of carrying out the project work, information (technical results) had to be passed along and exchanged freely. Tardy and faulty communications on the part of one line engineer had the following effects:

1. Reduced effectiveness of planning
2. Tended to retard related work or other line engineers
3. Tended to complicate project leader's job of coordinating project activities

Untimely Cutoff—General Cutoff Considerations. Each of the chief engineers claimed that the typical project leader did not know how to administer proper cutoff of technical effort and experimentation, which tended to make project planning less reliable. The following were given as reasons:

1. Desire to be technically perfect
2. Personal technical interest of line engineers
3. Willingness to optimistically regard technical difficulties in order to guard line engineer's reputation
4. Desire for recognition and sense of accomplishment afforded by technical victory
5. Low predictability

Support for items (3) and (4) above was found in the fact that all nine project leaders stated that scientific accomplishment and recognition was the prime interest of both themselves and the line engineers. Each of the project leaders felt that he was always compromising technical interests and felt that perhaps work was cut off too soon and that more experimentation should continue in order to achieve the desired technical results. In short, the project leaders felt they were cutting off too early whereas in the same instances the chief engineers thought otherwise. According to the chief engineers, the cutoff decision was essentially a balancing of economical and technical considerations. Although they agreed that a cutoff decision finally rested with themselves, the chief engineers felt that the project leader could help by making appropriate recommendations.

The chief engineers regarded the following factors as important when considering a typical cutoff:

1. Extent of time delay on total project
2. Probability of experimental success
3. Over-all effect on total technical success of project

During the interviews, the chief engineers refused to give a typical example of a cutoff decision describing the net technical advantage to the project, and the incremental cost and time effects.

On the other hand, the chief engineers agreed that there were some mitigating factors supporting the continuation of some experimentation, these factors being as follows:

1. Reduces engineer's frustration through satisfaction of curiosity.
2. Allows possibility of discovery.
3. Mollifies personnel for good general relations.
4. Provides experience.

Improper Handling of Project Personnel. The chief engineers claimed that good planning was important in handling and directing project personnel. Conversely, proper handling of personnel helped bring about good planning. In their opinion a clear knowledge of relevant project assignments worked into a well-designed over-all project program which helped keep project personnel well informed and better directed towards desired objectives. During the intermittent review phases of the budgetary process, a group that was kept well aware of the project program reduced the chance of untimely availability of material and facilities and of possible continuance of unmeaningful experimentation.

The handling of project personnel was an important and delicate task for the project leader according to the chief engineer. The slightest provocation could easily damage personnel relationships and, consequently, would tend to reduce the effectiveness of the project team in planning and doing its work. The project leader, as coordinator, was in a good position to police and keep relations at a workable level, providing he knew what was going on. Earlier in this chapter it was pointed out that communications were usually faulty. This in itself provided a basis for ruffled feelings and a general tendency towards a breakdown of relations. Faulty technical information, passed from one line engineer to another, could not only easily delay the project work but could also embarrass the recipient line engineer. Any reflection on one's professional ability was seriously regarded by the individual concerned. The chief engineers typically felt that the sensitive handling of people was very important to the project leader. One chief engineer pointed out that because project work was a group effort and generally encountered many difficulties, there was great latitude for inadvertently casting blame. This chief engineer cited an example of a project leader who insisted on using a new way to convert laboratory-prepared silicon into a semiconductor. The final transistor failed. The project leader blamed the failure on the basic material prepared by the chemist. The chief engineer finally determined that the blame lay with the project leader's new process. According to the chief engineer, the project leader was "on the spot" with the project personnel because he put the blame on the line engineer. Another example was given by a project leader who pointed to the fact that because some project leaders had a better relationship with some line engineers, these project leaders get preferential treatment from those line engineers, a fact that sometimes tended to delay the work of other projects. This project leader also pointed out the difficulty in proving an allegation of favoritism, and the further danger in reporting favoritism to the chief engineer for fear of alienating the line engineer involved.

Project Leader Burdened by Detail. Two of the three chief engineers claimed that the project leaders were burdened with too much detail. They felt that project leaders must discern the importance of things and apply their time and attention accordingly. One of these chief engineers stated that the project leader was the last man in the chain of management, and as a result, many things were usually passed down to him. Both of these chief engineers felt that the project leader was not relatively skilled in administration and budgetary matters. In only one of these companies were the project leaders required to participate in management training courses given by the company. In all three companies, however, they were encouraged to take university-level courses with emphasis on the relevant sciences.

Project Leader's Need for a Scheduling Device

Central to planning was the function of scheduling, which fundamentally requires a device to measure input factors and a method to present the plans as a function of time. Eight of the nine reporting project leaders were cognizant of the need for a scheduling device. They emphasized the point that even in the face of low predictability, a scheduling scheme was needed to allocate the line engineer's time over the next working period (one month). Even though such a schedule might have been inaccurate, it would have provided the project leader with some notion as to the timing of work and would have helped him to better coordinate and dovetail project activities. In the three companies studied there was no evidence that such a schedule for line engineers existed.

The project leaders realized all too well that an attempt to schedule line engineers meant defining and measuring the input factors of the creative process. The project leaders expressed an objection to project scheduling, similar to that expressed by the line engineers, because low predictability made schedules inaccurate and they did not want to be held to such schedules. They also feared that any forecasting device might tend to be time-consuming and thereby detract their attention from other project problems. In spite of these practical difficulties, the project leader recognized the need for some sort of scheduling device.

Vague Specifications Precluding Scheduling According to each of six project leaders reporting from two of the companies, some of the project specifications were not spelled out enough to permit the formulation of reliable schedules. Earlier in this chapter, an example of vague specifications was described. The project leaders typically objected to the principle of setting specifications in a vague manner. They insisted that vague specifications had the following results:

1. Complicated the technical work
2. Prolonged the work load
3. Increased uncertainty

They claimed that minor variations in any of the specifications had a marked effect on their total experimental design, which in turn affected project completion date and cost. They pointed out that as a result, input factors were proportionately complicated, usually calling for more knowledge, more engineering time, and perhaps more technical ability and more advanced technical devices. In one company, technical specifications were never spelled out vaguely even though they were sometimes set high and then altered as dictated by later-acquired technical knowledge. All the project leaders in this company agreed that clear-cut technical specification changes were important to scheduling. In their experience each specification change altered their laboratory work assignments; but they reiterated that between specification changes the technical objectives were specifically (not vaguely) set and tended to make their planning a good deal less complicated.

Difficulties of Scheduling The project leaders felt that a number of benefits would accrue from a comprehensive scheduling device.

Eight of the nine project leaders from the three companies studied cited the following benefits:

1. Arrest some effects of low predictability.
2. Aid in arranging sequences and chronological order (reduce "bumping").
3. Aid in setting time for services (establish more reliable arrangements with services).
4. Estimated time versus actual time would aid in evaluating progress.
5. Alleviate crash programs.

The project leaders pointed to the multiplicity of experimentation and to the need for meshing the acquired results in order to plan and to initiate the ensuing experiments. In their minds, it was necessary not only to mesh knowledge but to arrange technical work assignments in a simultaneous fashion if possible in order to fulfill their responsibility for concluding the project as soon as possible. To do this, they realized the need for measuring and programming the input factors (material, facilities, and line engineer time). In each of the companies reporting, a substantial amount of material and facilities used were requisitioned by the line engineers. According to the project leaders, three factors impeding scheduling prevailed:

1. Line engineers' monthly work per project was scheduled not by calendar days, but only as a percentage of a whole month's time.
2. Project leader was not permitted to utilize line engineers on a day-to-day basis.
3. Line engineers were not interchangeable.

First of all, a percentage of the line engineer's total monthly man-hours was assigned to the project by the functional head and the chief engineer (Table 7-1). According to the project leader, the actual distribution of the line engineer's time and the decision as to when certain work assignments would begin and end depended on the following factors:

1. Forecasting ability of the line engineer
2. Technical ability of the line engineer
3. Effect of other work assignments of the line engineer, especially any projects "in trouble"

TABLE 7-1
Distribution of Manpower over Projects in Percent of Total Monthly Time

				Project designation			
Names	153	131	148	STAC	133	155	Total
1	10		10				20
2	5	50	5				60
3					85	15	100
4					80	20	100
5							
6	50[a]		50				100
7				60			60
8	50		50				100
9	15		25			25	65
10	15	25	15		20	25	100
11					100		100
12			10		40	50	100
13	20		20	20			60
14							
15		50			15	35	100
16			25		20	25	70
17						100	100
18	5		95[a]				100
19			15		30[a]	15	60
20	5		15			15	35
21	25		30			40	95
22					15	75[a]	90
23	50		50				100
24		50					50
25	10		10		10		30
26	100						100
27					80		80
Total Manpower (No. of Men)	3.6	1.75	4.1	1.8	4.25	4.25	19.75

[a]Project leader for this project.

Secondly, the project leaders in each of the companies were not in direct charge of the line engineers, with the following results:

1. Project leader could not utilize line engineers according to project day-to-day needs
2. Project leader could not demand calendar-time-based work schedules from line engineers

In conjunction with the above, the project leaders were not compelled to approve material requisitions, work orders, and other service requests, though each felt that if he had so desired, it would have been possible. In one company the project leaders insisted on countersigning expensive project expenditures.

Thirdly, each of the project leaders felt that only with great difficulty could an assigned line engineer be replaced by another skilled in the same discipline. Several reasons were given in support of this feeling:

1. New line engineer would have to study and absorb a great deal of technical information already possessed by the original line engineer.
2. New line engineer might well propose a different approach and surmise of problems, which would need examination and study.
3. The above (1 and 2) would alter input parameters and therefore be time-consuming and costly.

The only formal time schedule the project leaders in each of the companies had was the target-type completion date denoted on the project technical proposal, along with target dates for major phases of the project. However, individual experiments conducted during the month usually were not scheduled in terms of setting their starting and finishing dates. Instead, their "scheduling" was confined to the stipulation of technical achievements expected from the experiments during the next month.

Implications

From the observations made concerning the project leader's role in the budgetary process, it was evident that some planning was under way at the project level but that more effective planning was needed. This need was also voiced by each of the chief engineers.

Chief Engineer's Performance Partially Dependent on Project Leader Planning Each chief engineer claimed that part of his own performance was evaluated on how well he was able to bring about technical results within the limits of the laboratory budget. In his opinion it was not difficult to stay within the total laboratory budget providing he kept his manpower force stable, stayed within reasonable limits of material and facility requirements, and kept overtime to a minimum. He felt that he could not, however, guarantee attaining the technical proposal objectives within the financial limits set by the laboratory budget. Hence, keeping within the limits of the laboratory budget was not necessarily any indication of technical progress. Budgeting per se was not absolutely needed for good planning and scheduling, but good budgeting usually depended on having good planning and scheduling.

Adherence to the individual project budget also did not mean that the technical goals were attained within the financial limits set by the budget. However, with the project budget it was easier to relate expenditures to technical events. The time function itself was the variable relating the budget to technical progress. For example, if in a $20,000, one-year project, a total of $10,000 had been expended, a major question would have been, Was it possible, with the remaining scheduled input (remaining funds translated into engineering man-hours), to complete the technical objectives within the remaining time? If the required number of man-hours projected beyond the remaining time, then more funds likewise would have been needed providing the manpower was available. Hence the time factor was an important consideration.

Each chief engineer depended on the assistance of the project leaders to guard against extended cutoff points and lack of sufficient planning associated with low predictability. The chief engineers raised the question, How much planning? They each realized that project technical proposals were too broad for direct translation into daily work assignments and that a more penetrating (but highly unpredictable) complex of project problems was needed. Although they produced no evidence of having tried, the chief engineers felt that a project budget, estimated from a moderate breakdown of problems developed from the project technical proposal, was probably more accurate than one translated from a more detailed complex of project technical problems. They felt that the myriad of subproblems and combinations of their solutions that would be obtained from a detailed exhaustive translation would defy reliable measurement and would tend to produce more uncertainty, especially the further the planning and scheduling extended into the future and the deeper it penetrated into the project's technical problems. Hence, in their opinion, a project budget developed from a translation of broad problems alone and adjusted for error on the basis of typical past performance of similar laboratory work would have produced a more accurate budget in less time than would have a more detailed approach.

Scheduling and Better Dovetailing of Project Activities Eight of the nine project leaders felt the need for a scheduling device; each believed that better dovetailing would tend to conserve engineering time, reduce difficulties in programming for the ensuing monthly period, reduce the use of crash programs, and help alleviate conditions of thinly-spread manpower.

Because of low predictability, time was of utmost importance. In many instances the technical projects were bound to the company's promotional program to establish a desired market position. Hence the timely completion of R & D, of pilot-run operations, and of successful transfer into the factory was necessary in order to secure the company its market position. As a result, each of the project leaders referred to the frequent use of crash programs to keep the project moving ahead. The incidence of crash programs was not accurately known. In spite of the use of crash programs, the project leaders reported that their projects usually varied approximately 25 percent over the originally estimated calendar timetable. They each claimed that the 25 percent variation would have been greater had not management usually reduced the project specifications in favor of an earlier termination date.

Scheduling and Minimizing Thinly Spread Manpower All of the project leaders in the three companies studied claimed that manpower was spread too thin. The major reasons given as most provoking this condition were as follows:

1. Competition
2. Current shortage of engineers and scientists
3. Low predictability
4. Backlog of work for engineers and scientists
5. Manpower not interchangeable

According to the project leaders, competition, among other factors, compelled management to have several projects simultaneously in process in order to maintain market position, because of the likelihood that some projects would not generate a salable product. They submitted that the line engineers and scientific specialists were usually behind in their work commitments. They ascribed this partly to too much work being in process and to low predictability.

The project leaders argued that with an excessive work load, the line engineers dissipated their energy and could not concentrate long enough in one given period to make timely, meaningful inroads on troubled work assignments. For example, if on a project estimated to require three man-months of effort, a line engineer was scheduled to devote only a fourth of his time, the project leader estimated that the job would take longer than twelve months because of the increased opportunity for delay in twelve months (as compared, say, with three months of full-time work). The laboratory was always experiencing an assorted number of exigencies. In addition, there would be slippage due to the line engineer's inability to devote a steady concentration of brain power; that is, every time the line engineer switched from one project to another, a certain amount of time would be lost in recovering to the same level of concentration as when he left that project. In my opinion, the project leaders were alluding to some sort of "mental dexterity." Typically, the line engineer who worked on two, and sometimes three, projects could have switched back and forth three to four times to the same project. The number of days between his "mental spurts" was difficult to estimate because it depended on the nature of the problem and the point at which he switched. The companies did not have a monthly work report for each day showing those projects worked on by one particular line engineer. The only report made available was one showing the distribution of total line engineer time over monthly periods (see Table 7-3, preceding section). Project leaders usually felt that if the line engineer could devote more time to fewer projects, the total length of elapsed time per project would tend to decrease.

One chief engineer theorized that if the laboratory worked on the principle of fewer projects arranged in tandem, the total output of completed projects for a given period of time with an equal number of men would have been at least as many and perhaps more than under the present system of scheduling projects simultaneously. He ascribed this to the elimination of "recovery time" and to aforementioned "mental dexterity." He felt that there would be an added benefit due to the absence of confusion created by simultaneous projects. This chief engineer was not able to schedule fewer projects because simultaneous scheduling was more flexible. Even though under the tandem method of scheduling, completed projects might be produced in substantially the same sequence as dictated by the marketing program, the tandem method lacked flexibility. Under simultaneous scheduling, for example, there was an opportunity to hold up one project and stress another. To illustrate further, according to the chief engineer, a greater number of projects provided a kind of insurance against serious project failures, and a means for absorbing manpower should some projects break through and terminate sooner or others be seriously delayed. Although these reasons are emergency kinds of values, their incidence in R & D laboratory work is highly prevalent, almost to the point of being routine.

Shorter Projects versus Longer Projects According to the experiences of each of the project leaders and chief engineers, the element of low predictability diminished as the project progressed and approached completion. The rate at which low predictability decreased over the course of the project was not known. Project leaders and chief engineers felt that the reason for the improvement of predictability was due to the accumulation of technical knowledge. In one of the companies, the projects were of the six-months-duration variety, in contrast to the other two companies, where projects generally ran from one year to one and one-half years. The project leaders in the company with the shorter-term projects did not see the necessity for using a scheduling device during the conduct of their projects, in contrast to the project leaders of the other companies. The former felt that their initial estimate of the project timetable was accurate enough, even though their method of estimating the project completion date was not basically any different. They ascribed the adequacy of their original project completion dates to the following:

1. Shorter duration time provided less opportunity for delay.
2. Abundance of needed knowledge was relatively greater (or amount of knowledge searched for was not relatively as great).
3. Network of problems and solutions was less complex.

Summary

The chief engineers wanted project leaders to do more planning; they pointed to the inadequacy of the project technical proposal in being too broad for day-to-day planning of work assignments. They highlighted the strong need for skill on the part of the project leaders in handling people and in building up a high level of genuine cooperation. The chief engineers felt that the project leaders needed to balance the economics of continued experimentation and technological benefits against the stifling of individual line engineer incentives to help bring about a more appropriate cutoff point.

The project leaders felt the need for a timetable device for roughly scheduling line engineer time on major experiments in order to better dovetail project activities and to help minimize the overburdening of manpower. As project work progressed, predictability improved. Budgeting was not absolutely needed for good planning and scheduling, but good budgeting depended on good planning and scheduling. Should any of the problems facing the project leader in the budgetary process with respect to planning and scheduling be lessened, the budget would become a more useful management tool to the project leader and to management.

▶▶▶▶ **8**

Organization and Communication

The purpose of this chapter is first, to show evidence of the various manifestations of the lack of direct authority of the typical project leader over project personnel and project work, and the prevalence of impediments to smooth communications among project personnel; and second, to discuss the implications of these limitations as they related to the project leader in the budgetary process and to management.

Project Leader and Responsibility for Project

The typical project leader was not completely responsible for his project. In earlier chapters the typical role of the project leader in the budgetary process was developed and shown to include such major responsibilities as planning project work, implementing project changes, and reporting technical progress. According to the project leaders, their major over-all responsibility was to coordinate the manifold activities of the project towards a planned conclusion. Some of the important activities involved in the process of coordinating the project, as described by the project leaders, are listed in Table 8-1. Within the framework of these coordinated responsibilities, it was incumbent upon the project leader, as shown in preceding chapters, to concern himself mainly with the tasks of keeping the information flowing between the interdisciplinary groups, fostering effective planning and scheduling, and expediting the dissolution of bottlenecks. A typical organization structure of the type visited for this study is shown in Figure 8-1. Table 8-1 shows which key personnel of the typical organization had prime responsibility in making the decisions concerning each of the project's main coordinating activities, as reported by all (nine) of the project leaders in the three companies

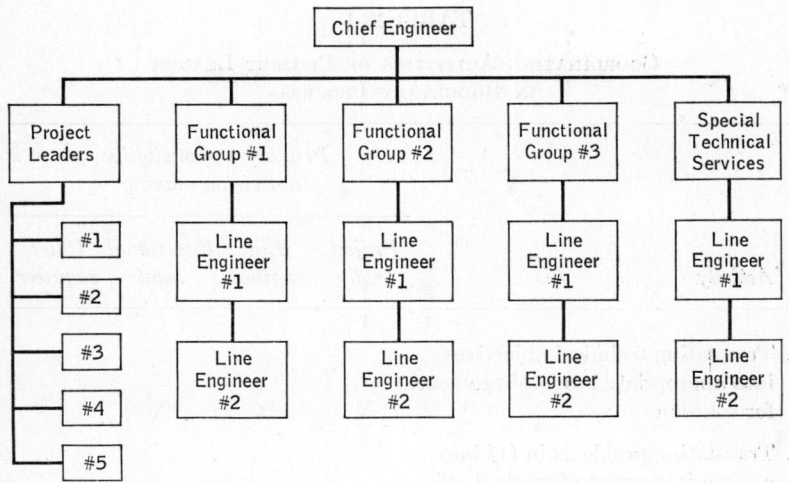

FIGURE 8-1. Typical laboratory organization structure.

studied. From Table 8-1 it can be seen that the project leaders shared in the decision making. Each of the project leaders recognized that he was not responsible entirely for technical results, project budgets, and project timetables. Project leaders felt that their responsibility was one of attempting to attain the best technical results within a reasonable length of time. In the eyes of management the typical project leader was a representative of project personnel and their problems, and also, conversely, represented management's attitude and ideas to project personnel.

Organizational Encumbrances

Lack of Authority of Project Leader over Line Engineers Each of the project leaders felt that in the course of performing their duties, they encountered several major encumbrances that hindered their adherence to the budgeted man-hour and timetable limits. According to the typical laboratory organization structure, the project leaders did not have direct authority over project personnel, a condition that the project leaders claimed retarded their efforts in coordinating the project activities because they could not assign and direct the line engineers. They pointed to the fact that the coordinating function called for taking into account the points of view and ideas of each of the principals, including line engineers, functional heads, and the

TABLE 8-1

Coordinating Activities of Project Leader in Budgetary Process

Activity	Primary responsibility in decision making			
	Project leader	Line engineer	Functional head	Chief engineer
1. Translating technical objectives into appropriate group of problems for solution	X	X	X	
2. Translating problems in (1) into appropriate group of methods of solution	X	X	X	
3. Planning and arranging for material and facility requirements	X	X		
4. Attempting to program near-simultaneous arrangement of technical work assignments	X	X		
5. Monitoring; troubleshooting for delays; progress reviews	X			
6. Making progress report to management (chief engineer)	X	X		
7. Maintaining flow of information among project personnel	X	X		
8. Determining experimental cutoff	X	X	X	X
9. Implementing changes ordered by management	X		X	

chief engineer. In addition, the faulty flow of information and the resistance to schedules of line engineers contributed further to the project leaders' difficulties in directing their projects to an expeditious conclusion. The project leaders were seriously concerned about the encumbered flow of technical information and the lack of interest and ability displayed by line engineers toward programming. Because of these encumbrances the project leaders felt that their performance and reputation did not rest within their full control.

The chief engineers felt that the lack of project leader authority over project personnel was a major factor in support of the importance of project leader know-how in handling people and the need for better project planning in order to improve project coordination. The project leaders also felt that because of the prevalence of low predictability, faulty communications, and the need for scheduling, their having direct control over line engineers would have improved the task of coordination. But they realized that direct control was not practical and would be costly simply because line engineers' full time on projects was not needed and idle time would result. Hence, without real organizational control over line engineers, each project leader recognized and pointed to the importance of teamwork.

Unity of command is generally considered good management practice; that is to say, no one individual should serve two bosses, because unity adds to the effectiveness of planning and aids in fixing responsibility for judgment and actions.[1] The project leader's job is somewhat analogous to that of the production control manager and the budget director in manufacturing. The responsibility of these manufacturing service groups is to coordinate the activities of production departments, but they usually do not have organizational authority over the people responsible for the production work. In contrast, control and coordination exercised by staff groups is more effective in production because of the higher certainty in forecasting work.

General Communication Process Although the heart of the communication process was the monthly review meeting, which is the subject matter of the next chapter, the general communication procedure will be described briefly here. In addition to the necessity for understandability of the information being transmitted, smooth communications depended upon the procedures for conveying information. As pointed out in the preceding chapter, "information" was the so-called product of R & D effort. The process for exchanging information on a timely basis was important because in practically every phase of the project leader's job of coordination, it was imperative to

---

[1] Ernest Dale, *Planning and Developing the Company Organization Structure*, Research Report No. 20. New York: American Management Association, 1957, p. 108.

receive adequate information for decision making and planning. For example, the communication process was started by the project leader receiving the project technical proposal; then, together with the line engineers, he interpreted and planned project work. Once the work was under way, the need arose for timely two-way feedback of information from project personnel to the project leader and then to the chief engineer for appropriate, timely corrective action. The vehicles for communication were personal contacts at will, both *ad hoc* and scheduled meetings, and reports. Although this procedure was adequate, it did not guarantee the adequacy of the information conveyed by virtue of the use of the vehicles alone. The project leader, as coordinator, was in a position to judge the appropriateness of the information. However, as was pointed out in Chapter 5, the basic understanding was often faulty and line engineers, because of personal motivations, often censored and biased their reports.

The difficulties that faced the project leader in understanding and in extracting information from line engineers will be discussed more fully in the next chapter. But even if the project leader had had organizational control over line engineers, these difficulties would not necessarily have improved. The lack of understanding between the project leader and the line engineers was a limitation that according to the project leader emphasized the need for high-level teamwork and good relations among project personnel.

Implications

Human Relations and Low Predictability Let it be assumed that low predictability was substantially improved and that it was possible to forecast effectively creative input and output. Under these conditions, even though effective planning would have made it possible to hold project personnel to forecasted targets, the following organizational and human relations problems would still have existed:

1. Checking up and ascertaining that line engineers were getting work done and that project work was moving in line with plans
2. Selecting compatible project personnel to insure teamwork
3. Fostering proper working climate

The process of ascertaining that line engineers were performing their work in line with plans and that they were feeding back adequate progress information will be discussed in greater detail in the next chapter.

Selection of Compatible Project Team An accurate forecasting technique would not necessarily have eliminated some of the problems emanating from human relations. For example, in each of the companies reporting, the chief engineers attempted to select and appoint project leaders on the basis of their general technical knowledge, affinity for planning, and their ability to handle and get along with people. Usually project leaders were selected from the ranks of line engineers who had demonstrated the necessary abilities. Some of the limitations facing the project leader indicated that all-round project leaders were in the minority. The desirable qualities of the typical project leader will be considered more fully as recommendations in Chapter 10. Line engineers were assigned by their respective functional heads and the chief engineer on the basis of technical ability and compatibility. Usually it was not possible to honor each request from project leaders for certain line engineers because not every one was free for assignment. It was not always possible to hire line engineers with desirable personality characteristics and high technical ability because of the national engineer shortage.

Limitations to Proper Working Climate The chief engineers and the project leaders agreed that the general atmosphere of the laboratory should be one of little pressure. They felt that pressure retarded the creative process and hence the expeditious output of the project team. Several factors, however, contributed toward the development of disconcerting pressure. For example, as was pointed out in an earlier chapter, line engineers along with project leaders resisted cutoff because it was opposed to some of their basic motivations for technical achievement and recognition. Then, too, the project leaders were uneasy with regard to scheduling and budgeting because limits based on inaccurate forecasting were thereby placed on their work assignments. The project leaders therefore felt that budgeting was inconsistent with a pressure-free working climate, even though they themselves might be allowed to help set limits. In addition, faulty communications contributed to the pressure because it tended to strain relations. On the other hand, the need for better communications, for more effective planning, and for a scheduling device became another area of strain. Emphasis on the need for high-level teamwork tended to increase the dependency of project personnel on one another, creating greater frustration. All the foregoing factors were sources of pressure in addition to those encountered from the uncertain nature of the technical work itself.

The project personnel were not completely unsympathetic towards the organizational requirements. The project leaders, along with the line engineers, were cognizant of the need for more accurate forecasting and more judicious use of manpower, because they realized that the company and, hence, the project must stay within the limits of the financial resources in order to make a profit. However, the project leaders admitted that their most important consideration was for meeting technical objectives.

Summary

The lack of direct authority over line engineers, about which the project leaders complained, tended to put more emphasis on the need for project leader ability to coordinate. Good coordination in turn prompted the need for more effective planning, scheduling, and handling of people, and for the maintenance of high-level teamwork. These factors, in part, developed the need for a good working climate in the laboratory. However, because of low predictability, project leaders and line engineers resisted project budgets. Hence, the desired working climate appeared to be inconsistent with the budgeting concept. Furthermore, the nonexistence of a scheduling device, because it impeded dovetailing of project activities and created an air of uncertainty, also appeared inconsistent with a good working climate. In addition, faulty communications, caused by the lack of adequate understanding and the difficulties in extracting and evaluating technical information, also strained relations. Good budgeting would not necessarily have alleviated the above limitations, but if they were alleviated, more effective budgeting would have developed.

Even if predictability increased substantially, it would not have been accompanied by a proportionate lessening of the problems of coordination, development of teamwork, and subsequent creation of a desirable working climate. Management recognized the need for a workable climate; and the project leaders and line engineers recognized that management's objective was to direct and conduct the project within the limits of budgetary resources. The project leaders, nevertheless, put more emphasis on achieving technical results rather than risk destroying the incentive of project personnel.

▶▶▶▶ **9**

Monthly Project-Progress Review

The purpose of this chapter is to show evidence of the lack of depth and breadth of the monthly progress review conducted by the project leader in the budgetary process, and to show the implications of this lack in regard to the project leader and management.

Monthly Progress Review as a Communication Device

The monthly project-progress review was essentially a device for communication designed to do the following:

1. Gather technological knowledge discovered to date
2. Check up on technical progress by matching technical achievements with project technical objectives
3. Exchange information among project personnel
4. Supply the basis for a monthly technical progress report to the chief engineer
5. Develop work assignments for line engineers for the following period

In Chapter 4, the procedure for the project-progress review was described; Table 9-1 shows some of the important factors related to the progress review as reported by the project leaders interviewed.

According to each of the project leaders, each progress-review meeting was preceded and supported by a network of informal meetings among the various project personnel. The monthly meeting was an official one at which time all subject matter of the informal meetings was summarized for the edification of all project personnel. The monthly progress-review process essentially fell into two basic phases:

95

TABLE 9-1

Factors Related to Monthly Progress-review Meetings

Factor description	Number of project leaders of 9 reporting	Number of companies of 3 reporting	Remarks
Purpose: To check progress	9	3	Over-all purpose to help coordinate project activities
Time per meeting: 1 to 2 hours	9	3	Each meeting supported by informal random meetings among various project personnel
Main subject: Technical events	9	3	Those transpired, in process, and contemplated
Project budget: Not considered	6	2	
Over-all project timetable: Not considered	6	2	

1. Gathering of technical information and evaluating and relating it to project technical objectives
2. Development of day-to-day work assignments needed to carry out the work of the project

In a sense, developed technical knowledge, an important element of the creative process, was defined, measured, and translated into the plan of work for the following month in terms of experiments to be done within the budgeted amounts of man-hours and material resources. This process was always in continuous operation by virtue of the regularly scheduled monthly review meetings and the supporting network of informal meetings.

Faulty Information from Line Engineers According to each of the project leaders, a major impediment confronting them in the initial phase of the review process was that they felt uncertain about having received all of the existing technical knowledge and experimental results from the line engineers. They each felt that the flow of information was inhibited by the basic motivations of the line engineers. For example, the project leaders felt that in the face of certain technical difficulties, the line engineers generally tended to continue their efforts rather than report the exact nature of the difficulty, for the following reasons:

1. Line engineer thought failure would be a strong reflection of his ability.
2. Line engineer hoped the difficulty ultimately would be resolved.
3. Line engineer feared a decision to cut off his experiment precluded a technical victory that would enhance his reputation.

The project leaders recognized the influence of these motivations in retarding the timely flow of information, and admitted that they had difficulty in working along with them.

Project Leader's Lack of Understanding of Other Disciplines The problem of understanding "what goes on" concerning the interdisciplinary work of the project was very important. Each of the line engineers, including the project leader, was professionally trained in one of the scientific disciplines. The extent to which the project work assignments penetrated into some of these disciplines was beyond the knowledge of the project leaders and of line engineers in other disciplines. For example, if the project leaders did not adequately understand a technical problem in their own area, then their judgment concerning its contribution to the over-all project objective was likely to be faulty. This condition also held true among the project personnel with respect to areas other than their own. The difficulty in understanding one another not only tended to inhibit the timely flow of information but very likely caused a distortion in the information.

The project leaders felt that pertinent technical information was not reaching them from the line engineer, a feeling that was partly due to lack of understanding and partly because the line engineers were usually too burdened with assignments to afford time to enlighten the project leaders. Moreover, the line engineers usually received meaningful technical advice from their respective functional heads and not from the project leaders, who lacked the necessary technical know-how. The project leaders' inability to offer meaningful technical advice precluded useful technical discussions with line engineers. However, more of the exact nature of technical difficulties would have been revealed by their engaging in such discussions.

The project leaders, not always having a meaningful understanding of the technical problems, were sometimes precluded from making effective evaluations. But the project leaders claimed that ultimately, the important technical events and problems inevitably emerged into view. This delayed emergence of the difficulties, however, was inconsistent with one of the objectives of the review process, which was to take timely remedial action. One project leader reported an incident where a line engineer withheld reporting technical difficulties, thereby implying success and near completion. Meanwhile, project funds were dispersed where necessary. As a result, when the difficulty was discovered, not enough funds remained to cover the proper solution of the problem: the project had to be refinanced.

Faulty Communications a Hindrance in Work Projections During the monthly review session, the planning and scheduling of project work for the next month took place. It was not enough for the project leaders to know what work was anticipated for the next month; they also needed to know whether the planned experiments could be accomplished within the limits of the budgeted man-hours. To make this evaluation, the project leader needed to know and understand the nature of the technical work involved, including the appropriate effectiveness of experimental methods. Because he lacked adequate understanding, the project leader depended on the line engineers to help make the evaluations. Although the work involved was not "blue sky," the technical issues required a sound understanding of the "engineering" exclusive to the disciplines. Since communications with line engineers were usually faulty, the project leader claimed it was difficult to gain adequate understanding quickly.

It was not even enough for project leaders to evaluate the feasibility of getting planned work done within the budgeted man-hours. They also needed to know "when" during the month the various experiments would be staged so that project activities and services could be dovetailed. Again, this information could best be estimated by the line engineers who were responsible for the work; but in view of low predictability, they were reluctant to make time forecasts for fear of being held to them by management. As was pointed out in Chapter 7, there was no evidence that functional group heads had detailed work schedules distributing the work of their line engineers to each project over calendar days.

Appropriate planning for timely requisitions concerning the acquisition of material, inexpensive equipment and facilities, and other services was another concern of the project leaders. Much of this planning was left to the line engineers because they knew more exactly the nature of their needs. The reluctance of line engineers to be scheduled emphasized all the more this planning on their part. The preceding method for planning material and facility needs was not wholly without fault. For example, one of the chief engineers related an incident where a line electrical engineer thought a line chemical engineer was going to initiate a work order for some test gear. When the actual need for the test equipment arose, it was not available. The chemical engineer had thought that since the electrical engineer was present at the same meeting, he would have initiated the proper request for the test gear. According to the chief engineer, the project leader should have checked on the alleged work order during the interim, but he failed to do so because he thought the matter was taken care of.

Implications

Nonconsideration of Over-all Project Timetable in Monthly Review

In earlier chapters and in the preceding sections of this chapter it was seen that the project leaders encountered various difficulties and impediments to scheduling, such as thinly spread manpower, line engineer resistance to schedules, and use of crash programs for project work which bumped their own work. The project leaders charged that the total project schedule, which showed a target completion date, was not adequate for day-to-day assignment of technical work. They claimed that a project schedule comprising the major experiments, and schedules showing the work load for each of the disciplinary areas did not exist. In this study there was no evidence that functional heads kept a formal schedule for the work of their individual line engineers. The functional head was aware of the work planned but did not have any kind of document showing the schedule. Each of the project leaders said that when two or more work assignments converged on one line engineer and/or the same laboratory equipment, the chief engineer was consulted to decide the priorities. According to the chief engineers, a priority list was set up balancing the following factors:

1. Which project was needed in the factory first.
2. Which project was nearer an important breakthrough.
3. Which experiments were shorter (shorter experiments were sometimes given higher priority to get them out of the way).

Because it was part of the project-progress review process to plan coordination of in-process and anticipated work load, the absence of a simple scheduling device created a situation of organized chaos.

Because of the general fear of being held to relatively inaccurate time schedules, the result mainly of low predictability (especially during the early and mid-point stages of a project), project leaders did not attempt to evaluate the remaining project calendar time in terms of progress during the regular monthly progress-review sessions. There was no system for scheduling by which calendar-time progress on individual major experiments could be related to the over-all project timetable through an intermediary level of subproject schedules. As the project neared completion, timetable evaluations were made for the over-all project, because by then low predictability had typically diminished and because the project completion date was usually synchronized with a production program.

The work of the next monthly period was planned and scheduled by the project leader in accordance with what could reasonably be accomplished within the man-hours budgeted for the project. Although the budget in terms of dollar figures was not used directly, the number of man-hours (the heart of the budget) specified by the budget gauged the amount of work programmed for the next period. Better planning and scheduling helped project personnel adhere to the budgeted man-hours, but better budgeting could not necessarily help produce better planning and scheduling.

Nonconsideration of Remaining Project Funds in Monthly Review
The preceding discussions indicated insufficient use of the project budget by the project leaders. The chief engineers stated that the project leaders were not skilled in the cost and budget areas; the project leaders recognized their lack of understanding of the budget and further claimed minimum interest because budgeting was not their complete responsibility. Each of the chief engineers felt that the project leaders did not know how to administer cutoff. They added that the cutoff decision involved a balancing of cost, time, and technical factors. As stated in an earlier chapter, the companies declined

to give a quantitative example of cutoff. An appropriate time and place for discussing cutoff decisions was during the progress-review sessions, but the general immunity of project leaders to budgetary considerations partially precluded this. Project leaders claimed it was difficult to use the total project budget in determining the cost feasibility on cutoff problems for individual experiments and on other various work-assignment alternatives. The project budget in each of these companies was a total dollar figure comprising man-hours, material, and miscellaneous-expense items. Project leaders said that the total project budget man-hours could not easily be used to indicate whether alternative experiments or corrective action in terms of man-hours was in line with the remaining financial resources of the project. The project leaders did not concern themselves with any kind of detailed budgetary scheme because they considered project budgeting to be inaccurate due to low predictability.

At the project level, many day-to-day decisions (including corrective action) were made. These decisions were not made on a comprehensive basis including the consideration of economic factors because the project leaders usually did not evaluate their actions in terms of remaining calendar time and remaining project resources. Although technical results were continually checked against technical goals by project personnel, such technical evaluations were not comprehensive enough to be helpful in trying to stay in line with project budgetary and timetable goals.

Summary

The monthly project-progress-review meeting, along with its supporting network of informal meetings among project personnel, was mainly a communication process that was used to check up on technical progress and to provide a basis for determining and programming the technical work load lying immediately ahead. The project leaders pointed to the difficulty in extracting gained technical knowledge from the project line engineers. The monthly programming that took place was by and large without the assistance of over-all time schedules and project budgets. The project leaders felt that although they lacked skill in budgeting, use of the budget was further precluded by the fact that the budget was not arranged in detail so as to be conducive to appropriate considerations. For example, in attempting to make cutoff decisions and cost judgments concerning alternatives, the total project budget was too broad to help in making meaningful evaluations. The lack of effective use of the budget tended to make the budget of less value to the project leader.

The absence of regular monthly timetable and budget evaluations prevented a comprehensive economic consideration of the routine corrective action taken by the project leader and the line engineers on their own. Without a monthly timetable and budget evaluation, it would be difficult to see how they could hope to stay much in line with the over-all project timetable and budget.

▶▶▶▶ **10**

Recommendations

In this chapter, recommendations will be submitted as to what can be done to improve the use of budgets as a management tool by the project leader. The first part of the chapter deals with recommended changes in the standard budgetary process, the latter part with specific recommendations to the project leaders and to management. In making recommendations to project leaders and to management, emphasis is given to their respective points of view concerning not only the specific recommendations made to them but the changes to the budgetary process as well.

Recommended Changes in Budgetary Process

The following changes are recommended in the standard budgetary process:

1. Addition of subproject budgets
2. Addition of a variance-analysis procedure
3. Addition of a scheduling device

In this section the discussion will be confined to the mechanics of the changes, the incremental time and effort of project personnel needed to implement the changes, and some of the obvious benefits accruing to the project leader and to management. The cost and effort of instituting the recommended changes to the budgetary process will be considered in the discussion of recommendations to management in the following section; acceptance is solely the responsibility of management, and the broad considerations of management adoption will be made then in the context of other recommendations. The alternative to the recommendation for subproject budgets, non-

103

dollar planning, is partially taken up in the project leader and management sections because of the important relationship it bears to their respective project-budget-oriented recommendations.

Subproject Budgeting In the standard budgetary process developed earlier in this study (Chap. 4), the project budget and timetable were estimated values established to represent the project in entirety. I propose that a budgetary scheme be adopted consisting of a network of subsidiary budgets and timetables covering each of the major sectors of the project. The process for forecasting the budget in the proposed system is identical to that in the standard budgetary process except that the proposed scheme has an added step for developing the subsidiary budgets of the project. In Table 10-1 the project-budget-formulation system is described; Operation 7 is the added step that covers the formulation of budgets and timetables for each of the major segments of the project.

In this proposed change, the project leader estimates the subproject budgets with the help of his line engineers. In the standard budgetary process, when the project is initially assigned, the project leader and the line engineers plan the technical work, and it is at this point that the planning is to be extended by developing subproject budgets from the appropriate translation of technical work into man-hours, dollars, and calendar time.

A Variance-Analysis Procedure and Broader Monthly Progress Reviews These subsidiary budgets and timetables are to be periodically checked and, if necessary, revised. Table 10-2 describes the monthly maintenance of progress (variance analysis) for the proposed budgetary network. Each month actual costs for each of the major project segments (problem areas) are gathered and reported to the project leader via the accounting department. In the meantime the timetables (one for each of the segments) are revised simultaneously. At this junction the project leader, together with the appropriate line engineer, translates the anticipated line activities into engineering man-hours, material, services, and facility needs. By use of a conversion factor, man-hours can be expressed in dollars. It may be better and simpler to show engineering time in man-hours and the other cost items in dollars, but in my opinion, the decision is optional for the project leader. So-called guesses would not be made for consumption by top management but for the project leader. The purpose of this information would be to provide the project leader with data that he would use in making unofficial budget and timetable revisions for his

TABLE 10-1
Formulation System of Project Budget

Operation	Performed by				
	Top management	Chief engineer	Functional head	Project leader	Line engineer
1. Prepare project technical proposal* and freeze same.	X	X			
2. Translate into broad technical problems (subprojects), each falling into one functional disciplinary group.		X	X	X	X
3. Translate each broad problem into major parts.			X	X	X
4. Translate each major part into technical problems and corresponding methods of solution.			X	X	X
5. Translate technical problems and methods of solution into requirements in terms of a. engineering man-hours b. materials c. facilities			X	X	X
6. Convert requirements (5a, 5b, 5c**) into a. dollars b. calendar time and consolidate to get grand summations for total project budget and timetable.		X			
7. Apply Steps 6a, 6b to each broad problem area (3) and consolidate to show budget as a function of calendar time.				X	

*If project leader was known (assigned) he was usually consulted.
**Exclude in making operating budget.

own use. Table 10-2 clearly shows that new estimates are periodically made concerning the balance of the work to be done. These balances are added to the calendar time and money (man-hours, material, etc.) already expended, the totals of which are compared with the original estimates. The differences are called revolving variances — one for calendar time and one for man-hours and cost. Depending on the degree of technical success for project work, the revolving variances may fluctuate from month to month.

Variance analysis detects unforeseen contingencies soon after they appear, which then in turn prompts more timely corrective action. Without a scanning device like variance analysis, which behaves as an early warning system, these contingencies tend to become discernible later. If the project leader detects a definite change or trend, he then consults with the line engineer as to the necessity of transmitting this information to the chief engineer. In this way the pressures of budgeting and scheduling are not imposed upon the project leader and line engineer by management but by their own planning. This proposed budgetary program makes it possible for the project leader to estimate the required amount of funds and time needed to complete the technical work of each major problem area. If these data are integrated on a project-wide basis, the total needs for project completion are known.

Nondollar Planning as an Alternative to Subproject Budgets In this section a nondollar planning practice used typically by the project leader is contrasted with subproject budgeting. The nondollar type of planning scheme involves the following:

1. Determination of technical work (experiments) to be done
2. Establishment of a network of anticipated experiments: long run — approximation of major work; short run — more specific definition of project work
   a. Sequence of intradisciplinary experiments
   b. Sequence of interdisciplinary experiments
3. Conversion of technical work to man-hours and establishment of percent distribution to each discipline (a guide as to monthly allocation of line engineer time in percent)

This kind of planning device establishes "what" has to be done but only part of "when" it has to be done. Specific calendar-time assignments are not made, which according to the project leaders, adds to the uncertainty in their planning of future work.

TABLE 10-2

Variance Analysis
Periodic Maintenance Process of Project Budget

Operation	Performed by		
	Accounting	Project leader	Line engineer
8. A. Prepare periodic actual cost to date per each broad problem area of project (3) (see Step 3, Table 10-1); send to project leader.	X		
B. Make periodic estimates of requirements to complete major problems in terms of a. man-hours b. materials c. facilities d. services.			X
9. Convert (8B) into dollars (per broad problem of project) needed to complete major problems.		X	
10. Add dollars expended to date (8A) to new estimated dollars needed to complete problem (8B) to get revised estimated total amount to be expended.		X	
11. Compare revised cost estimate (10) with original estimate (7) (see Table 10-1) to get revolving cost variance.		X	
12. Convert estimated man-hours needed (8B,a) into new estimated calendar-time needed to complete major problems.		X	
13. Compare revised timetable (12) with original timetable (7) (Table 10-1) to get revolving calendar-time variance.		X	
14. Analyze (11) and (13).		X	
15. Consult together on analysis and mutually determine what information will be passed on to chief engineer.		X	X

By and large, the nondollar planning device does not consider the adequacy of remaining funds (engineering man-hours) and elapsed calendar time to finish the project work. Although the proposed subproject budgets and corresponding variance analyses are uncertain, they do represent an estimate of the best "guess" and therefore reflect the latest, most up-to-the-minute thinking. The result is a broadening of the monthly progress review and puts the project leader in a better position to make the following appraisals:

1. Evaluation of financial cutoff point on questionable experimentation
2. Evaluation of proposed alternative work assignments in each major problem area (with respect to the remaining man-hours and funds available)
3. Evaluation of anticipated changes to the project (with respect to the remaining man-hours and funds available)

The variance analysis of the elapsed-time function in the proposed recommendations helps to improve the allocation of man-hours and funds over calendar time and helps to better evaluate alternatives and their effects on the total project timetable, which, again, adds to the scope of the monthly progress review. This variance analysis would also be useful in the following instances:

1. In making timely transfers to factory
2. In timely planning for new R & D projects

Proposed Changes to Scheduling System Scheduling is a device that helps the project leader dovetail the various interdisciplinary activities of his project in accordance with calendar-time requirements, and is an organic part of the proposed subproject budgets and variance-analysis procedure. As for its relationship to budgeting, even though the plan for technical work to be done and the corresponding number of engineering man-hours is known, it is quite possible, because of the uncertainty, that the allocation of these man-hours (material and facility requirements also) can be applied either too early or too late, setting off a chain reaction of costly delays and/or costly bottlenecks. It should be added at this point that the proper allocation of resources depends partly on the project leader's scientific know-how.

Alternative Scheduling Devices There are three ways by which a schedule for line engineer's work can be devised:

1. Allocating a percentage of each line engineer's total monthly working hours to each project
2. Scheduling a block of time (one man-month) per line engineer per project
3. Scheduling line engineer time as needed by projects, based on priority rank of projects and the maintenance of minimum idle time and project delay

In the standard budgetary process, Plan 1 above was the system used. Its main drawback was that project leaders were not instrumental in determining the distribution of line engineer time, and the assigning of this time to specific calendar periods was not scheduled.

As for Plan 2, according to the structure of the typical project observed in this study, one stage of a particular experiment usually takes several days and its continuance depends upon information from other disciplinary areas, which in turn need the results of this experiment to develop the further-needed information. This intermittent characteristic of the interdisciplinary work creates unnecessary idle time under the "block of time" allocation system.

Plan 3 primarily allocates line engineer time over calendar time on the basis of priority rank of projects, and their corresponding estimates of calendar-time required. This appears to be the most efficient plan if the calendar-time scheduling can be done.

In the standard budgetary process, the distribution of the percentage of the line engineer's monthly time was made at a monthly meeting of the chief engineer and his functional heads. I propose that at this meeting the scope be broadened to include decision making as to the priority ranking of projects and the estimated calendar-time assignments corresponding to the work of line engineers. It is further proposed that the line engineer man-hours be estimated together — that is, with the line engineers present — because they are the ones who do the work. I also recommend that the project leaders be included at this meeting so that their knowledge and ideas can materially benefit the decisions reached. The application of the proposed scheduling device in the context of low predictability and its effect on creativity is considered more fully in relation to other recommendations in the section of this chapter dealing with recommendations to project leaders. In preparation for this meeting and in development of the elapsed-time estimates for the project work, which typically involve four or five major experiments per month, the project leader probably would be required to spend an additional four to five hours monthly (including the time for the meeting).

Benefits of the Proposals as a Whole The proposed devices are not a panacea for low predictability. As a matter of fact they will not reduce low predictability per se. What they can do is to alert the project leader to make more timely considerations as technical events so dictate. The planning pressure exerted by the proposed recommendation would tend to reduce anxiety because the project leader and line engineer would be better forewarned of events and might better interpret the effects. Essentially, the perpetually developed cost and calendar-time data make this possible.

The procedures suggested are like those employed by a navigator who changes his compass heading in order to expeditiously reach his destination in the face of magnetic field changes and variable winds. Changes are made because more recent information has been acquired, rendering preceding knowledge obsolete. The navigator doesn't say, "There is no sense in determining new positions and headings because they will only be changed a little later on"; the element of change is consistent with the concept of navigation. Similarly in the proposed budgetary scheme, change is consistent with the concept of the system because the new information is generally more reliable.

Some of the benefits to be accrued from the proposed recommendation are the following:

1. Compels project leader and line engineers to take a closer look at their work
2. Integrates line engineers into the budget-planning and time-scheduling function
3. Closes some of the gap between project leader and line engineer
4. Helps the making of better cutoff decisions
5. Gives project leader an added dimension with which he can better describe technical events to the chief engineer and management
6. Provides a good basis for check list for material and facility requirements
7. Tends to reduce number of crash programs
8. Provides a basis for dimensioning thinly spread manpower problem

Although the proposed budgetary scheme is not an absolute substitute for the lack of project leader authority over line engineers, it does give the project leader an effective tool, the proper use of which should give him better control over activities. Moreover, the benefits should provide another means, and a justification, for the project leader to get more acquainted with the line engineer's work. To the extent that the recommendations would compel the project leader to earn more of the specific technical activities, they should provide a basis for further understanding, and hence, would tend to improve retarded communications.

These proposed changes also provide the project leader with dimensions that management best understands — namely, time and money. With the new budgetary and scheduling devices the project leader can translate such problems as faulty service, inadequate funds, manpower shortages, inadequate space, inadequate facilities, and inadequate market data more decisively into terms of time and money. Hence the substance of his communication to management would be more meaningfully presented. These advantages in turn help broaden the coverage of monthly project-progress reviews and reports.

How Much Extra Administrative Effort Would Be Required by Proposed Changes? Under the proposed recommendations the accounting department and the project leaders along with the line engineers will be called upon to give of their time. Just how much time will be best surmised by looking at each group's requirement separately in terms of what they would have to do.

Accounting Group. In the typical budgetary system, the accounting department kept cost data on a monthly and a year-to-date basis. These were broken down essentially into engineering man-hours and material costs. To comply with the recommendations, the subproject-budget data should be arranged in the same way as total-project data in the typical process. The accounting group needs to do only the following:

1. Identify accrued incoming cost and man-hour data with corresponding phase of subproject
2. Report the monthly and year-to-date data by going one step further and showing subproject data in the same way as total-project data

The incremental effort essentially depends upon the number of subprojects. By using a number designation for a project and an alphabetical code for subprojects, Step 1 above would be almost effortless. As for Step 2, the effort increases by a factor equal to the number of subprojects, because the data that are reported and assembled for the project will be needed for each subproject. The laboratories observed in this study averaged about 5 projects and each project averaged 4 subphases. This explodes into 20 sets of data. Each set typically has two major breaks — one marked *budget* and the other *actual* — with each break showing *this month* and *year to date* (total of 4 columns). The volume of basic input data (time cards and material requisitions) would not change, but rather would be arranged into 80 additional aggregates. In accounting by hand, this represents approximately half a day of one clerk's time and much less time with data-processing equipment.

Project Leader and Line Engineers. There are a few demands for additional time facing the project leader and line engineers, since the proposed scheduling scheme and the development of variances require effort not called for under the standard budgetary process.

The two-hour formal monthly meeting for project leaders and functional group heads under the proposed scheduling system is one principal source for additional effort. Since the main objective of this meeting would be the allocation of calendar time for line engineers and for laboratory apparatus, especially in instances where there are conflicts between projects, it seems reasonable to expect that each participant of this meeting would spend no more than two to three hours to prepare for and carry out the decisions of the meeting.

Another principal source for additional effort results from the development of monthly variance analysis. The project leader and the line engineers, on a regular monthly basis, would have specifically to address themselves to a consideration of the need for more or less time and funds to complete the work of the project. Since these variances would be for their own private consumption, they would be free of the concern as to management's reaction. If work proceeds according to plan, then the effort for variance analysis would be minimum.

Now if after a series of monthly variance analyses, a definite gap between the original budget and the latest estimate occurs, or if a serious delay or breakthrough develops, the need for a revision of budget would depend on the probability of the variance in calendar time and funds being absorbed before the project terminates. If in the judgment of the project leader the variance would not be absorbed, then presumably management would be informed. Management is more concerned in being forewarned of an impending revision and its order of magnitude and consequently the frequency of revision may not be increased. Under the standard budgetary process, major changes were ordinarily translated into a revision, hence the incremental effort under the proposed procedures appears to be nothing much more than the time given to the monthly conduct of variance analysis. Moreover, the monthly variance analysis would tend to decrease the effort that would otherwise be needed to translate major unforeseen project events into a revision. In my opinion the variance analysis probably would not increase the total amount of time devoted to estimating revisions in the long run, but rather would spread out the effort over time (via the series of variance analyses) and would compel the project leader and line engineers to spend more frequent brief periods making estimates. The greater expenditure of time due to the increase in frequency, in my opinion, would be offset by briefer periods needed each time.

Can the Proposed Changes to the Budgetary Process Be Justified? There are two basic considerations in weighing the question of justification. One is to balance the cost and time for implementing and applying the proposed variance analysis and scheduling systems against the benefits to be derived. The second and contingent on the first is the consideration, Should the proposed changes be made at all?

The preceding discussion in this chapter seems to indicate that the incremental time per man per project would be no more than four to five hours per month. The benefits, on the other hand, seem to show better use of budgeting by the project leader in making allocation decisions (manpower and funds over calendar time). If the project leader's planning effectiveness is improved, he has a better basis for communicating with management and project personnel. The closer working relationships thereby encouraged among project personnel would tend to help project leaders partly to overcome some of the problems arising out of his lack of organizational authority over line engineers. An underlying advantage would be the project leader's improved capability to cope with the element of low predictability because of the better basis for more timely corrective action. In my opinion the achievement of only a portion of the benefits listed above would more than justify the additional few hours expended by the accounting group and project personnel.

Even though there appears to be adequate justification for the proposed subproject budgets, scheduling scheme, and related variance analysis, the question of how practical these recommendations are should also be considered. There is a widely accepted notion that budgeting and scheduling tend to curb engineering incentive and creativity. How applicable is this notion in laboratories typical of the ones observed in this study?

If engineering man-hours, funds, and calendar time are tight, there will be a tendency to be careful as to the allocation of these economic factors because the company must operate profitably. If man-hours, funds, and calendar time are not tight, the need to keep resources in line still exists because it is the proper management approach. In order not to risk stifling creativity, the tendency to provide the proper management approach may lose emphasis, however. In both instances the issue seems to be a balancing of creativity needed against the availability of resources. Hence, in the type of laboratories observed in this study, how much creative ability was needed? A careful examination of the type of projects observed showed that initially some creative ability (not of the basic research type) was needed, but for the bulk of the project work, fruitful results could be brought about by prudent application of engineering know-how because low predictability diminished with progress. The degree to which thorough budgeting and scheduling should be applied to a project in its various stages will be covered later in this chapter in the section devoted to recommendations to management.

The proposed scheduling device should help the project leader to dovetail the various activities of the project. The budgetary process would be more useful through the more efficient allocation of budgeted man-hours, materials, and machine-hours of the general purpose experimental apparatus. Even though the benefits would outweigh the few additional hours of project leader time required, should the changes to the scheduling system be made? This question can be answered by taking into account the effectiveness of the scheduling device in light of low predictability, its effect on individual creativity, and its effect on the working climate of the laboratory. The broad consideration of these factors will be taken up later in this chapter, as previously mentioned. It will then be seen that the net effect on creativity and working climate does not preclude its adoption, providing it is used at the proper time in the course of project development.

Reactions of the chief engineers and project leaders to the proposed recommendations for subproject budgets, variance analysis, and the scheduling scheme showed the existence of some doubt as to whether the project leaders could develop variance analyses and subproject schedules and make effective use of them because of lack of know-how. The chief engineers expressed their fear that project leaders might apportion more time to working out the budget than in getting the project work completed. They agreed that benefits to project leaders would accrue if the recommendations were properly administered. One chief engineer, however, felt that his project leaders should be spared of budgetary matters so that all their time could be given to getting the project work done.

Project leaders recognized their own lack of understanding of the budgetary concept. This, coupled with the element of low predictability, developed a hands-off attitude on their behalf. Project leaders also felt that their use of the principle of minimum cost (alternative experiments selected on the basis of fewest required man-hours) helped keep costs in line. Although this method indicated the least expensive alternative, it did not tell them whether future allocations (cost, man-hours) were in line or beyond the budgeted amount.

In my opinion the recommendations concerning the subproject budgets, the variance analysis, and the scheduling device are feasible, require relatively little effort in contrast to benefits derived, and are practical, if (and only if) project leaders are properly trained in the use of budgets and in relevant scientific and personnel management areas. The matter of this kind of training is discussed further in the next section.

Recommendations to Project Leaders

In view of the limitations confronting the project leader in the standard budgetary process, there are some definite kinds of action he can take that would make the budgetary process more useful to him and to management. The following is a list of recommended actions:

1. Adopt a budgetary scheme
2. Learn more about
   a. The science and technical areas involving his project
   b. Budgetary skills
   c. Personnel management and human relations

Proposed Project-Budgetary Scheme for Project Leader So that he may gain the benefits of the budgetary process, I recommend that the project leader adopt the budgetary scheme described earlier in this chapter. Budgeting is a planning device. Although budgeting is not the only way to program a technical project, it does have the added feature of tying together man-hours, material usage, and calendar time with dollars, giving the plan the dimension of cost. Many day-to-day decisions governing the project activities and made at the project level should take into account such basic economic considerations as the following:

1. Adequacy of remaining funds to complete project work (alternative-choice decisions)
2. Advisability of making a cutoff-point determination

It seems to me that the failure to explicitly recognize economics-oriented considerations reduces the chances of staying within limits of the company's financial resources. This fact alone suggests that the project leader should adopt a subproject-oriented budget. It is doubtful that management, because of its volume of work, would be able to give adequate economic attention on the basis of the monthly progress reports. The thirty days between reports to management is rather substantial, considering the number of day-to-day decisions being made at the project level. Furthermore, the monthly reports are made after the fact. Finally, because of low predictability, the future-projected work in monthly reports is relatively uncertain. The variance-analysis device, operated and used by the project leader, should give the budgetary process an added advantage over a nondollar-type planning program by helping him to make more timely considerations. The advantages that the project leader should derive from the proposed subproject budgetary scheme were specified earlier in this chapter. Not only would the benefits of the proposed budgetary device be useful to the project leader but the improved coordination of the project should benefit the chief engineer and top management as well. As a matter of fact, with more effective planning at the project level, the work of the laboratory would be better synchronized with the marketing, financial, and manufacturing activities of the company.

Should Project Leader Use Nondollar Plans and Schedules? The benefits of budgeting as a planning device, which is merely an extension of a nondollar-type plan (work to be done converted into man-hours and then dollars), were shown in the preceding discussion. While a typical nondollar-planning scheme spares the project leader of cost considerations, it creates a gap over an area of company activity (project-level work) where economic considerations are partially left ignored. It was pointed out that the chief engineer and top management have too much work of their own to consider the economics of the daily project decisions. Therefore, it seems to me that the project leader, as project coordinator, is in the best position to take into account the economic considerations.

Should Project Leader Adopt Proposed Scheme at All? The benefits of the proposed budgetary scheme for the project leader discussed earlier in this chapter more than compensate for the four to five hours monthly that he would spend implementing it. A further question is, Is the absolute value of the benefits significant? Essentially, the benefits accruing from the proposed scheme provide a better basis for closer working relationships with line engineers and therefore better communications, as well as for the planning and dovetailing of project activities that are essentially his job of project coordination. These benefits also tend to minimize the use of crash programs and the spreading thin of engineering manpower.

Collectively the benefits are significant. Therefore, it appears that the project leader would be justified in adopting the proposed budgetary system. In discussing this idea with the project leaders they expressed their doubts as to applicability, however, because they did not understand the budgetary process. In my opinion, if the project leader understood the budgetary concept, he would readily discern its usefulness and value to him. I recommend that the project leader adopt the proposed budgetary scheme after having some training in its use. It is highly improbable that the project leader would undertake the adoption of the proposed budgetary scheme without appropriate help (in the form of preparation and interpretation of reports) from the accounting department, which would not be forthcoming without management's approval. Management's support and role in the proposed budgetary scheme is taken up in a later section of this chapter.

Proposed Additional Training for Project Leader The project leader's job is essentially one of planning and coordinating the various interdisciplinary technical activities of the project, with the needed help of the project line engineer, within budget limits. To do this effectively he must have some understanding of the nature of the technical problems and methodology in each of the scientific disciplinary areas, in budgeting, and in personnel management and human relations. Later in this section the need for more training, its relationship to budgeting, and the alternative ways open to the project leader are developed. The scope of this training is taken up later in the section on recommendation to management, when the cost and the practicability to management are fully developed. It should be kept in mind in the immediate discussion that the training program proposed involves one two-hour training session per week. The distribution of subject matter is approximately 20 contact hours in budgeting, 60 hours in technical subjects, and 60 hours for the combined personnel management and human relations training. It is estimated that the participants would devote no more than 2 to 4 hours per week on their own time in preparation for training sessions.

Project Leader's Need for Additional Technical Know-how. The project budget is a translation of the technical plan and method of work into financial terms, and an allocation of resources (man-hours, dollars) over calendar time. If parts of the technical work are poorly considered, then not only the technical plan of work but also the monthly allocation of engineering time and funds is proportionally less effective. Under these conditions the budget is of little value as a planning and control device. Project leaders have recognized their need for keeping abreast of technical developments. Line engineers, as observed in this study, have indicated their reluctance to discuss technical events with project leaders because the latter showed a lack of awareness of some of the technical problems and of the effectiveness of the related methods of problem solution.

In the standard budgetary process the project leader and the line engineers planned and scheduled the technical work in-process in accordance with the budgeted man-hours and funds. The project leader not only relied on his technical know-how but on his communications on technical matters with line engineers as well as his communications with management. The recommended changes to the budgetary process described earlier in this chapter (subproject budgets, variance analysis, and a scheduling device) depend primarily on the project leader's and line engineer's technical know-how.

The lack of adequate understanding of technical work by the project leader increased the probability of allocating too little or too much in man-hours, funds, and calendar time to the technical work of the project. In addition, faulty monthly progress reports tended to pass on to management. By definition the relationships of factors like man-hours, funds, and calendar time to anticipated technical events are essential parts of the budgetary process and the proposed budgetary changes.

How Much Technical Know-how? First, it must be remembered that the project leader's engineering training is typically in only one of the scientific disciplinary areas. Therefore, because of this typical educational background, the project leader does not possess a formal working knowledge of other disciplines. Because it is difficult to determine how much and what technical knowledge is needed to effectively program a project, it is proportionally difficult to advise project leaders on how much more scientific knowledge they need. Probably the project leader himself can best determine this, with perhaps some help from the chief engineer, because the project leader is the only one aware of what he does not know. In my opinion the project leader must have enough technical knowledge to appreciate and evaluate the scientific problems and events so that he may understand and communicate better with project personnel and may organize and direct the subproject budgets and schedules. He must be able to conceptualize the general aspects of the technical events so that basic criteria governing the allocation of man-hours, funds, and calendar time can be reasonably determined and estimated. Even though he has the line engineers on whom he can, and must, rely heavily, nevertheless, the project leader himself must have a feel for what the latest technological practices can do. This tends to assure that basic communications are not hopelessly abandoned by the line engineers. The theory and/or basic technical principles change very slowly in comparison with applied methodologies. Hence, if project leaders keep abreast with the faster-changing major methods and develop basic general notions as to what to expect as to effectiveness, and as to the man-hours and time requirements for the major methods involved, I believe a broad basis for adequate communications would prevail.

Project Leader's Need for Additional Budgeting Know-how. In my opinion it would be difficult to get the project leaders to adopt any project-budgetary system because of their lack of confidence in its use due to low predictability and their lack of understanding. If the project leaders are to make effective use of budgeting such as has been proposed, it is imperative that the project leader first learn more about budgeting and the skills required.

Training in Personnel Management and Human Relations. The

project leader's major responsibilities involve activities performed by line engineers, which he must coordinate. Furthermore, the project leader has no direct organizational authority over the line engineers.

What is the relationship of training in personnel management and human relations to the improvement of the use of budgeting by the project leader? In examining the structure and nature of the project team, let us assume that the project leader's lack of direct authority over line engineers does not exist. Line engineers each have separate "bosses" and are held together as a project team only by the common goals of the project in which their individual work is interrelated, and they are dependent on the timely exchange of technical data for the normal process of work. Also, each considers his own work as extremely important, because technical accomplishment and recognition are the line engineer's high rewards. Lags in crossflow of information between line engineers are generally viewed with very little tolerance by the delayed line engineer because he considers these as impediments to his achievements. The interactions among project personnel form a potential arena for two-way tensions, as illustrated by the preceding example. The project leader, as a coordinator, must not hinder the process of interaction but keep it as free as possible from impediments. If the process of interaction breaks down, the result is little or no timely flow of information between individual line engineers and with their project leader. Hence, in chain-reaction form, the planning mechanism and the budgetary process are adversely affected.

What kinds of action can the project leader take? As a project coordinator, the project leader must strive to keep the interaction among project personnel at a good working level by attempting to encourage a workable structure of communication, responsibility, and authority for the project team and its members. This task, then, involves the area of personnel management.

Even though a workable structure may be developed, the project leader, in developing work assignments together with his line engineers, in coordinating the allocation of line engineer time over future periods, and in encouraging a sound basis for smooth flow of information, must avoid difficulties arising from either repellent individual or group behavioral characteristics. This responsibility takes the project leader into the field of human relations.

From poor communications and faulty human relations among project personnel can come inefficiencies in the planning of work and the allocation of resources. Hence the basis for budgeting tends to become less reliable. It is seen that even with direct organizational authority over project personnel by the project leader, the project leader is not spared of responsibility in his role in the budgetary process.

If we bring back the element of the project leader's lack of organizational control, he has the added problem of using relatively more persuasion. If project personnel reported to the project leader, there would be more of a tendency to follow his wishes. A comparison of the project leader with the production control manager may clarify the relationship of his lack of authority within the budgetary process. The production control manager also does not have line responsibility over production personnel, yet his production schedules are effectively administered. In my opinion this is true because the certainty in forecasting production work schedules is relatively high. In contrast, the element of certainty in forecasting project budgets and work allocations is relatively low, hence the project personnel cannot be easily held to budgetary targets. The element of low predictability aggravates the lack of authority limitation on the project leader. If the concept of variance analysis is used, the early warning aspect can reduce the adverse effects of low predictability in budgeting. This in turn renders the element of lack of direct authority more tenable to the project leader.

In the human organizational mix of the project team, the project leader is its work coordinator. In his educational engineering curriculum he probably received no training in the handling of people, and since this factor bears important relationships to budgeting, I feel that he must learn more about personnel administration and human relations. Because he leads the project and coordinates the activities of relevant personnel, he plays an important role in the development and conduct of a conducive working climate. What he can do to encourage a good working atmosphere is difficult for him to know. Some of the areas embracing desirable working conditions are the following:

1. Project leader must help to provide services to line engineers:
    a. Information and status of project and progress.
    b. Timely services, material, and facilities.
2. As a member of the management team, project leader must accurately impart management directives.
3. Project leader must acquire line engineer confidence.

Alternative Training Plans. There are three basic ways open to the project leader in developing breadth and depth of his technical knowledge, budgeting skills, and know-how in the areas of personnel management and human relations:

1. Self-education:
    a. Consult with and learn from line engineers.
    b. Consult with and learn from company personnel.
2. University evening courses.
3. A comprehensive company-sponsored training program.

There is some question as to the practicability and certainty of the first two alternatives. The reasons are as follows:

1. Project leader adherence to self-organized training is doubtful because of family obligations and other personal work which might take precedence.
2. Lack of competent educational supervision.

The fields of personnel management and human relations, unlike courses in scientific areas, are relatively too foreign and complex for most of the project leaders to acquire an adequate, meaningful understanding on their own. For technical subjects, in contrast, his basic courses in engineering provide at least a bridgehead for understanding related fields. Also, left on his own, the project leader lacks the benefits of formal instruction.

On the other hand, university courses, supervised by competent teachers, could be very effective except that the project leader would have to finance the cost and take the courses on his own time. Moreover, it may be difficult to find university courses coinciding specifically with the relevant individual needs.

The company-sponsored training plan seems to be the most practical one for the project leader for the following reasons:

1. Project leader would not finance training.
2. Training hours except for class preparations would be confined to company time.
3. Project leader's family and personal obligations would not be a deterrent.
4. Courses would be designed to more nearly fit project requirements.
5. Courses would be competently supervised, therefore more effective.

In the event that the company should not adopt a training program, then the university-courses plan is the more effective second choice, except that if the project leader provides time for evening course work, he may very well expend his time on engineering courses rather than on nonengineering ones. If the decision were left to himself, there is the possibility that the project leader would select the self-education alternative because of the no-cost and the on-company-time advantages. But this is the least effective approach.

Should Project Leader Take Additional Training at All? If the project leader does not take additional training in the suggested fields, the following are some of the consequences that may result:

1. Decreasing awareness and know-how of project technical work would tend to produce faulty planning and faulty coordination of interdisciplinary project activities:
    a. Faulty communications with project personnel.
    b. Faulty human relations, tending to make the allocation of resources unreliable.
2. Little or no budgeting know-how would preclude use of budgeting.

Therefore, adequate project leader training in the suggested areas should improve his use of the budget in the coordination of project activities. In my opinion the benefits gained outweigh the few hours a week spent by the project leader in training.

Would it be possible for the project leader to acquire the necessary know-how simply in the course of normal contact with appropriate company personnel? As for budgeting know-how, the subject matter is not that difficult, making it possible; but as for technical, personnel management, and human relations training, the task would become progressively more difficult. Under a formal training program the participant has a better chance of getting proper orientation of the subject matter and will probably learn more — and more quickly.

With competent instruction and adequate training time, this program would be worthwhile to the project leader only if he participates conscientiously; otherwise the training program becomes ineffectual. All of the project leaders in this study recognized the importance of teamwork, properly handling people, and technical know-how, and admitted their lack of understanding of budgeting. This evidence indicates that the project leaders would be very likely to welcome the training program if it were offered.

Recommendations to Management (Chief Engineer)

This study has revealed justification for action by the chief engineer and/or top management to make the budgetary process more useful to the project leader and to themselves. I therefore recommend that the following be done:

1. Avoid vague specifications.
2. Set up and adopt subproject-oriented budgets and schedules with project leader in charge.
3. Adopt training program in technical topics, budgeting, personnel management, and human relations.
4. Improve the basis for selection of project leaders, despite engineer shortage.

Avoid Vague Specifications A *specification* is a description of the technical objectives of a project decided by top management together with the chief engineer. Specifications set the values for the desired geometry, chemistry, and electrical performance characteristics. In Chapter 5 it was pointed out that specifications were often spelled out vaguely, and that vague specifications generally added to the element of uncertainty. A specification can be vague, not as a specific value, but as one that may fall within a range of values or be stated in somewhat indefinite terms, such as "Attain up to 1000 megacycles for frequency." Specifications set in this manner call for several stages of experimentation. In the actual case of the above example, each successive stage was geared to attain a higher frequency value until a value less than 1000 megacycles but acceptable to management was attained. This led to excessive experimentation and frequent back-and-forth consultations with management to see if attained values were acceptable. Conditions such as these add to the general uncertainty of spelling out the project work. The budget and schedule, which depend on the plan of work, become less effective. Some reasons given for vague specifications are the following:

1. End use of product not specifically known
2. Specifications of competitive products not known
3. Deliberate secrecy of specifications for competitive reasons

Therefore there are three categories into which projects typically fall:

1. Certainty as to end specifications but secrecy deliberately maintained

Recommendations to Management (Chief Engineer)   125

2. Uncertainty as to end specifications
3. Certainty as to end specifications with no secrecy

Alternative Approaches — Dummy Specifications. If the project falls into either of the first two categories above, it seems to me that management has essentially two alternatives in circumventing the use of vague specifications:

1. Establishing a dummy value for the specification and changing it when deemed appropriate
2. Allowing vague specifications until specification values can be specifically established

The use of dummy specifications has the advantage of enabling definition of technical problems and their relative methods of solution with sharper focus. This allows the project leader to plan the technical work and the ensuing subproject budgets and schedules with less uncertainty.

Should Dummy Specifications Be Used at All? One disadvantage of the dummy-specification alternative is that the specification values may be set too high or too low. If they are too low, the company loses the opportunity for a better end product by tending to hold back engineering incentive. If they are too high, the company could spend unnecessary engineering time and money. On the other hand, by using the best-effort approach, that is, allowing vague specifications, there are inefficiencies. Under this latter system the specification values are not pinpointed. Arbitrary values are set, and once reached, trigger off the setting of another group of higher values. The best-effort principle tends to encourage a multiplicity of experimentation to reach still higher specification values. If a higher technical goal had been set originally, then perhaps a few of the earlier rounds of experiments could have been avoided.

Although it is difficult to compare the magnitudes of the inefficiencies of the two alternatives, it seems that the dummy-specification plan offers a more orderly basis for project planning and budgeting and also gives the project leader some notion as to what management wants.

When Should Thorough Planning Begin in Context of Low Predictability? Even though it appears that the dummy-specification approach is better, the plan of work would still be uncertain because of the element of low predictability. This study has shown that low predictability has permeated through every facet of project work; it has also been shown that as technical work progressed, low predictability diminished. In actuality there is no definite way to reduce low predictability. However, having engineers with the ability and knowhow to work with and adjust to it would help minimize its unfavorable effects. Project budgeting and scheduling increase the possibility of making more timely work plans and desirable corrective adjustments, thus providing a means for coping with the element of low predictability. The question is, As low predictability moves from a relatively high point to a lower point during the conduct of the project, how thorough should the planning, budgeting, and scheduling be?

In my opinion there are three possible approaches to this question:

1. It may be efficient to do a reasonably thorough planning job at the time the project is initiated.
2. It may be more efficient to wait until the nature of the project is well developed before attempting thorough planning.
3. It may be more efficient to divide project into two phases:
   a. Phase 1 — broad-base planning to develop data and knowledge for better definition of project technical objectives;
   b. Phase 2 — thorough planning at this time to achieve project objectives.

Usually at the beginning phases of project work, the technical specifications, problems to solve, and related methods of solution cannot be completely spelled out and are therefore vague. Any attempt at thorough planning during this stage would be relatively incomplete and hence the planning effort would be inefficiently applied. If thorough planning is attempted after the unknowns can be spelled out rather well, then the following possible risks are run:

1. The point has passed when thorough planning could have begun.
2. Too much work has transpired with accruing inefficiencies because of the untimely application of thorough planning.

The third approach appears to have the advantage of rather efficiently determining that point when thorough planning should begin. This determination involves the balancing of the following factors and considerations:

1. Probability — the chance for defining unknowns sufficiently to begin thorough planning
2. Resources — funds, engineering man-hours, and calendar time
3. Benefits — better planning, better dovetailing of activities, more efficient allocation of resources.
4. Creativity — ability of engineering manpower to bring about technical achievements

The practicability, cost, and resulting benefits to management for balancing the above factors and determining the proper thorough-planning point will be taken up in the next section.

Set Up and Adopt Subproject Budgets and Schedules I recommend that management (chief engineer) set up and adopt subproject budgets and schedules in accordance with the recommendation for doing so made earlier in this chapter. The benefits to the project leader and budgetary process have already been described. In addition to these benefits, management would gain the advantages of better planning, more efficient use of resources, and the integration of economic considerations into project activities.

Usually the project leader was not consulted during the formulation and approval stages of his project. When he was assigned a project, he gave only perfunctory consideration to the project budget and timetable. In order to foster more project leader planning, the chief engineer should insist, via a written report, on the project leader's careful assessment of the cost and elapsed time elements of the project at the time he is initially assigned to lead the project. Although the project leaders seemed to be unmindful of weighted time and cost considerations when assigned a project, they were very reluctant to accept the chief engineer's budget and timetable. If the chief engineer insists on the project leader's careful consideration of time and cost factors, and if the project leader is encouraged to adopt subproject budgets, management could augment its own estimation of budgetary and timetable limits by establishing a better basis for integrating budget views with those of the project leader.

Cost of Subproject Budgeting to Management. In a previous section of this chapter it was pointed out that project leaders would spend an additional five hours per month, and functional heads and line engineers each an additional three hours a month to use the subproject budgets and conduct variance analysis. With the average size laboratory such as the type observed in this study, there are five project leaders, four functional heads, and twenty-five line engineers. Assuming an average salary rate of $5 per hour, the additional time is equivalent to approximately $3500 per year after deduction of federal income tax, which in reality may not all comprise an out-of-pocket cost. Since this time is fragmentary (few hours monthly per man) and because engineers generally work in spurts, all of this time may not replace useful time.

Should Management Adopt Subproject Budgets and Schedules at All? In this discussion, subproject budgets, scheduling, and variance analysis are the organs of thorough planning. It is apparent that the benefits to management should greatly outweigh the investment of a few hours.

The degree and amount of planning for one situation is not likely to be appropriate to another. The nature of the company's resources, in terms of the adequacy of funds, and the nature of the particular project, in terms of its technical difficulties, have a bearing on how to plan.

If resources are tight and probability low, generally the application of thorough planning may endanger the much-needed creativity. If resources are relatively abundant and probability again low, there is less inclination to apply thorough planning in order to not curb creativity. The issue seems to be the balancing of the inefficiencies that would result from curbed creativity versus the inefficiencies that would be brought on by thorough planning. Stating it a little differently, the question seems to be, How much more can the company afford to spend to encourage creativity? However, it should be kept in mind that when resources are tight and the need for creativity is high, the engineers generally show willingness to economize. Now the issue becomes one of balancing the inefficiencies resulting from budgeting when probability is low versus the inefficiencies from lack of thorough planning. In this instance there is no real choice. Therefore, in the early stages of a project, when probability is low and the need for creativity high, it appears that thorough planning should not be applied until a point is reached when technical specifications, problem definitions, and technical methods can be spelled out. Of course, the project leader should be trained to accept and use the subproject budgeting and scheduling devices.

Adopt Training Program for Project Leaders In an earlier section of this chapter, additional training in relevant technical areas, in budgeting, and in personnel management and human relations was shown to be needed and beneficial to the project leader in the use of budgets. In this section the scope of the training, the time, and the cost to management are considered.

Scope of Courses. The technical course should involve some of the relevant theory and related technical methodology, with specific reference to limitations and the time required for applications. From this course, the project leader should acquire increased knowledge of the effectiveness of various methods in order to intelligently assess probabilities for technical success. Perhaps more emphasis should be given to methods and techniques, because engineering techniques change more often than scientific theory. In my opinion a four-credit-hour, one-semester course equivalent to 60 contact hours would be adequate to cover the needed technical knowledge in the two or three fields related to the project leader's own area.

Training in budgeting should involve a working knowledge of the mechanics of subproject budgeting, the conversion of the plan of work to man-hours, and the scheduling of calendar time. The training should also include an appreciation of the benefits of budgeting to the project leader and to management, in general, and in the coordination of project activities. Since this material would not be difficult to understand, it could be handled in approximately 20 contact hours.

A course in personnel management should deal with the problems of organizing people into groups, with specific reference to lines of responsibility and authority. This should help the project leader in organizing the allocation and the exchange of work among project personnel. Specific training in human relations should include the study of individual and group behavioral characteristics, which should help the project leader in encouraging a conducive working climate and good teamwork. Since the project leader is not likely to have had formal training in this complex area, this material could be covered in a four-credit-hour, one-semester type of course, or the equivalent of 60 contact hours.

Cost of Courses. These courses together total 140 contact hours, and if given on the basis of two hours per week, the training would take approximately 70 weeks. In my opinion competent instruction could be acquired at $150 per two-hour session, which would cost the company $5000 after federal income taxes. Since through observation and discussion it was learned that the turnover rate for project leaders averaged three years, new project leaders would not miss the training if the courses were given at this rate (every three years). On this basis, the training courses would cost the company an average of $1500 per year.

Assuming the laboratory is of a size equal to the typical laboratory visited in this study, and assuming all the project leaders (5) and key line engineers (15) are allowed to take the course, the man-hours lost represents one man-week of company time over one and one-half years. But since this time is spread over 20 men, it is not the same as one man being absent from his job. Referring back to a similar point made earlier, the few hours per week lost is not likely to represent valuable work time of the participants in all instances.

Alternatives. In an earlier section of this chapter, the alternatives of university courses, self-education, and a company-sponsored training program were discussed. The first two alternatives each have the following disadvantages:

1. Less likelihood of project leader participation
2. Courses not tailor-made and, therefore, pertinent concepts may not be appropriately stressed; learning time may be longer

The company-sponsored program appears to be the most practical even though it means cost and time to management, because this alternative gives the project leaders uniform training in the same period of time.

Should Management Adopt Training Program at All? Added training for project leaders is supported by the following:

1. The need to implement author's recommendations for more project leader participation in budgeting and scheduling
2. The project leaders' lack of know-how in training areas
3. The project leaders' need to do a better job
4. The need to establish a better appreciation for nonengineering (administrative) activities

From the preceding discussion it also appears that the benefits accrued by the project leader are quite likely to more than compensate to management for the investment of cost and time.

The project leaders interviewed tended to minimize their shortcomings with respect to administrative ability. Because of their technical professional background and interests, they subjectively cared less for administrative duties. Also, management's strong emphasis on technological ability minimized the importance of administrative factors such as budgeting and human relations. Hence I feel that management should encourage administrative training.

In my opinion the training program would not be beyond the project leader's capability, because of his demonstrated intelligence and because the subject matter is familiar to him and directly related to the things he does on the job. Moreover, the training sessions would cover one subject at a time, necessitating only one homework preparation.

Despite the receptiveness of the chief engineers and project leaders toward additional company-sponsored training (as mentioned in Chapter 7) its success would depend almost entirely on the quality of instruction. A fee of $150 per training session would be more than enough to acquire competent instruction.

Selection of Project Leaders in Face of National Engineer Shortage

If high-caliber engineers can be acquired by the company, the quality of technical work and general project performance will be improved. Management, therefore, should be more selective and careful in hiring and promoting line engineers to the project leader position. This is so despite the fact that efforts to do so are very likely to be encumbered by the nation-wide shortage of engineers.

There are fundamentally two basic things needed to improve the basis for selection:

1. To better know the characteristics needed for the job.
2. To attract a large enough group of candidates from which to select project leaders.

How can these fundamentals be applied to the process of getting project leaders? Because the project leaders are picked from the fixed line engineer ranks, the emphasis must be not only to look for line engineers displaying the best project leader potential but also to induce more of such persons to become project leaders. The following steps may be helpful:

1. Point to increased scope, responsibility, and value to the company of the project leader position.
2. Give recognition to good budgeting and scheduling and make it part of salary-increase formula.
3. Point to training program as free, organized way for personal improvement.
4. Look for background and qualities showing interest and

affinity for budgeting, scheduling, personnel management, and human relations; and for good general engineering background.

However, it is unlikely that these points alone would attract the major portion of recently graduated engineers and graduating seniors because they are more likely to be interested in professional, technical development and not administrative acumen. A possible appeal to these inexperienced engineers would be the working-climate factor, although this alone would again not be enough to attract them. In recruiting experienced engineers, however, the four points mentioned above would tend to be more appealing and thereby take on added significance. Although these suggestions broaden the recruiting approach, they may not produce a marked increase in applicants; but since the involved cost and effort to management would be nil, the steps should be adopted.

Because the chances of improving the caliber of personnel via direct recruitment appears to be marginal, the need for management to develop its own personnel and to provide a means for better work performance grows in value. Hence, the recommendations made to management in this chapter gain an added importance.

▶▶▶▶ **11**

Summary of Findings

The purpose of this chapter is to reflect in summary form (1) the main aspects of the project leader's role in the budgetary process in the context of his use of budgeting as a management tool, (2) the main limitations that faced the project leader in the budgetary process, (3) the implications of findings as they relate to the project leader in his use of budgeting and to management, and (4) specific recommendations to help alleviate some of the project leader's limitations.

Project Leader's Role in Budgeting

According to the typical budgetary process in the companies studied, the following were the major features of the project leader's role:

1. The project leader did not formulate the original project budget.
2. If management knew who was to be the project leader before initial formulation of a project, he was usually consulted in the general programming of project problems.
3. The project leader did not have responsibility for approving the project budget at the time he assumed responsibility for the project.
4. When assigned a project, the project leader accepted the technical proposal, project timetable, and total-project budget without critical questioning.
5. The project leader reported technical progress monthly.
6. The project leader made recommendations for technical changes.

133

7. The chief engineer and top management approved all changes recommended by the project leader.
8. The project leader did not make a cost analysis or relate cost relationships to technical progress.
9. The project leader did not make a timetable analysis or relate time schedules to technical progress.
10. The project leader implemented all approved changes.
11. The project leader applied the principle of minimum cost in decisions involving alternative choices.

In my opinion, the typical project leader's main responsibility dealt with coordinating the project activities. This involved technical decisions as well as administrative ones. No less than 70 percent of the project leader's time was spent on administration. In each of the companies, project leaders did some engineering on their projects, and in two of the companies approximately 30 percent of their work was engineering.

The chief engineers explained that the project leaders were not brought into the formulation and approval stages of the project simply because they did not know who the project leaders would be at the time of formulation. If they were known, they were consulted. The project leaders, on the other hand, were indifferent to time and budget factors when originally assigned a project. They were more concerned with the technical features, questions of feasibility, and technical methodology. Their general feeling was that because of low predictability, changes in timetable and cost were inaccurate, and therefore it was not worth their while to make cost and timetable investigations.

However, the project leader was well aware that his over-all task was one of expeditious coordination, preserving engineering man-hours and keeping costs to a minimum. From the project progress-review process he acquired what information he could to help coordinate project activities. He realized the importance of his monthly progress reports to the chief engineer and top management, who depended on these reports to evaluate progress, to recommend relevant changes to the project, and to help keep laboratory activities in line with company resources and objectives. The project leader knew the importance of good coordination because he realized the following:

1. Excessive time delays disrupted the company's market posi-

tion and gave competing laboratories an edge for being first with a new product.
2. Excessive time delays held back and reduced the total output of the laboratory.
3. Excessive time delays and costs unfavorably altered the company's return on investment schedule.
4. Casual attitudes developed an undesirable working climate and gave rise to undesirable practices:
   a. Tardy availability of services, material, and facilities.
   b. Frequent use of crash programs.
   c. Lack of meaningful understanding of line engineers' work and problems.

Limitations That Faced the Project Leader

Many of the project leader's coordinating activities were related to the project budget. However, within the existing budget procedures it was not possible for him to relate these activities meaningfully to the project budget. The following is a list of some of the major limitations that the project leader felt impeded his role in making fullest use of the budgetary process in carrying out his responsibilities:

1. Low predictability
2. Lack of an effective scheduling device
3. Lack of authority over project personnel, resulting in:
   a. Lack of full confidence of project personnel
   b. Difficulties in creating strong teamwork

The following is a list of some of the major limitations that the chief engineers felt impeded the project leader's role in the budgetary process:

1. Insufficient, shallow planning
2. Strong need for "know-how" in handling people

The following is a list of some of the major limitations that the author felt impeded the project leader's use of the budgetary process:

1. Faulty or retarded communications
2. Omission of project timetable from review process
3. Omission of project budget from review process

Recommendations to Project Leader

In view of his role in the typical budgetary process and the limitations facing him, the following are specific recommendations made to the project leader to improve his use of budgeting:

1. Learn more about the scientific and technical problems involved in his project.
2. Formulate project budget and timetable when assigned and submit to chief engineer for approval.
3. Adopt the recommended project budgetary and scheduling system, including
    a. A subproject budgeting and scheduling device.
    b. A variance-analysis system for cost (man-hours, materials) and timetable.
    c. Commencement of thorough planning in early stage of project when technical specifications, technical problems, and methods can be reasonably spelled out.
4. Learn more about budgetary skills.
5. Learn more about personnel administration and human relations.

Budgeting would not necessarily improve low predictability. Budgeting should, however, help the project leader cope with low predictability and adjust to its effects on a more timely basis. The variance-analysis scheme provides this advantage because of its early warning characteristics. If adopted, the above recommendations should accomplish the following:

1. Provide a tool for thorough planning, tying in the timely and appropriate allocation of resources.
2. Suggest a basis for balancing the efficiencies resulting from the timely employment of thorough planning against the inefficiencies of strained creativity and working climate.
3. Provide a basis for closer working relationships for project leaders and line engineers to better understand and communicate with one another.
4. Provide a basis for dimensioning the problem of thinly spread manpower and for reducing the use of crash programs.

The recommended training for project leaders should make them more aware of the technical, personnel management, and human relations issues. This should help bring about better budgeting and improved administrative ability, and should lead the project leader to appreciate the value of budgeting as a useful management tool.

Recommendations to Management

The recommendations to the project leader cannot be implemented without the support of management. It is therefore recommended that management adopt the same subproject budget and scheduling devices proposed to project leaders, and in addition, provide the needed accounting services and allow the necessary time for meetings. It is also recommended that management adopt the training program for project leaders in the technical, budgeting, personnel management, and human relations areas. Another proposal is that management require project leaders, when first assigned a project, to formulate a project budget and timetable for management's approval.

Implications of Management Rejection of Recommendations If management does not adopt these recommendations, it is unlikely that the project leaders can or will follow the recommendations made to them. Some of the implications of management rejection of the recommendations are listed below:

1. Deprives the project leader of a basis to cope with low predictability.
2. Deprives the project leader of a basis to make better cutoff decisions.
3. Prevents a more comprehensive consideration (cost-manhours, timetable) of project progress and future plan of work, because of lack of calendar-time and budget considerations during project leader's monthly progress review.
4. Deprives the project leader of the use of budgeting as a thorough planning device.
5. Deprives the project leader of a scheduling device that would more reliably distribute work load and better dovetail project activities, thereby partially helping overcome his lack of organizational authority over line engineers.
6. Does not encourage the improvement of faulty communications to and from the project leader.
7. Deprives the project leader of a practical way to acquire additional training in related technical areas, personnel management, human relations, and budgeting, through which more effective budgeting should result.

General Discussion

The problems and issues developed in this study do not appear to be basically different from those generally found prevailing throughout industrial R & D. Based on authoritative sources, it appears that some of the findings concerning planning, budgeting, and scheduling are also not unique to the companies visited in this study.

Careful examination of the limitations facing the project leader shows them all to be interrelated. This is as it should be, since all deal with the project leader in the budgetary process. In this study, for example, there is strong evidence that more planning was needed at the project level and that the planning being done was typically confined only to the technical work and was not much concerned with such items as cost, time, and human relations. I feel, however, that an attempt should be made to find several feasible ways of doing the technical work and to program these alternatives in line with the resources and objectives of the company in order that the chosen way would be one giving optimum results with a minimum expenditure of resources. In my opinion a comprehensive approach such as this would invariably require a high level of cooperation among project personnel and would therefore call for the development and use by project personnel of a budgetary scheme, improved communications, and a general working climate generating a high degree of cooperation. But as Dr. Vannevar Bush states, "There is no faster way to get rid of money than by ill-conducted or ill-planned research [and development]."[1]

Evidence from this study indicates that there was definite resistance against any kind of restrictions on project personnel. For example, project leaders felt that budgeting and scheduling imposed pressures on project personnel, and that because of low predictability, these pressures were inconsistent with a good working climate. In my opinion, the process of research and development itself is full of pressure. The line engineer and the scientist generally feel these pressures because they are surrounded by the element of uncertainty. They are in search of answers about which they know very little. As James B. Conant so ably said, "There are always many variables in an experiment. Failure to identify the significant variables . . . will vitiate the result. Often it is not easy to answer a simple question unambiguously

---

[1] Dr. Vannevar Bush, *Science and Business*. Address at Rutgers University, New Brunswick, N. J., 1958, p. 2.

by experiment. Erroneous observations or interpretations of experiments frequently persist...."[2] On the other hand, evidence from this study points out that budgeting and scheduling are additional sources of pressure and in my mind no different in the manifestation of frustrations. The main difference, however, lies in the attitudes and actions of the scientists and engineers toward the budgetary concept.

Allegedly, there appear to be two sources of pressure. It has been stated that the anxiety that produces pressure in doing research and development work is not the same thing as the fear that is produced by the pressure from budgets and schedules. The defensive attitude developed by the fear-oriented pressure, in contrast to the anxiety-based pressure, is incompatible with effective creative work.[3] As illustrated by Jules D. Porsche, "Their [engineers'] security is threatened ... [because a] potential reduction in budgets means likelihood of less frequent salary raises and decreased opportunities for advancement. The net result ... [is] curtailment of creative thinking."[4]

It was observed in this study that unlike in their research and development work, there was no positive action taken by the engineers to learn more about and solve the problems of budgeting. In the technical area they fought and reasonably overcame uncertainty, but in the budgetary area there was little similar effort.

This study reveals that the scientists and engineers did not understand budgeting, and as a result, lacked skill in its use. It is therefore recommended in this study that project leaders be trained in budgeting in order to increase its effective use. As David R. Anderson states, "It is important that the concept of the budget as a financial expression of an operating plan be understood clearly by all members of management who make use of it."[5] C. Argyris, whose study is in the context of the factory, feels that when budgets are not understood, people develop incorrect notions and think of budgets as confining gadgets for management. He also feels that budgeting must be accepted for what it is by the people who use it and that they must

---

[2]James B. Conant, *On Understanding Science*. New Haven, Conn.: Yale University Press, 1947, p. 104.

[3]Jules D. Porsche, *Creative Ability: Its Role in the Search for New Products*, Special Report No. 6. New York: American Management Association, 1955, p. 34.

[4]*Ibid.*, p. 36.

[5]David R. Anderson, "Practical Controllership." Homewood, Ill.: Richard D. Irwin, Inc., 1951, p. 102.

know its appropriate use and implications; to accomplish this he suggests training. He further states that because of the limiting effects of budgeting on the work and responsibilities of people, and because of these people's variety of harmful reactions, those who use budgets should be trained in human relations.[6]

This study also shows that budgeting and scheduling are needed and can be effectively applied. This need is not unique to the companies visited in the study.[7] Both Vannevar Bush and Howard K. Nason have stated that research and development can and should be scheduled.[8] Jules D. Porsche adds, "My conviction is that there is an inverse relationship between the scope of creative work and the extent to which pressure will be effective.... It is possible to expedite output of scientists."[9] Since Porsche considers budgeting as a source of pressure, his preceding statement implies that as creativity diminishes, budgeting could be employed. The present study reveals that it should be more efficient to employ thorough planning after technical specifications and technical problems and methods are reasonably known and spelled out. H. J. Finison has commented as follows: "When a project cannot be planned, based on today's knowledge, it is well to carry out an exploratory program ... [in order to] gain a better understanding as to what some of the unknown factors are...."[10]

Summary

At least 70 percent of the typical project leader's work observed in this study was administration. In standard budgetary process, his lack of ability in personnel administration and budgetary skills was pronounced. In my opinion, the project leader can cope with these deficiencies by seeking and acquiring proper training either

[6] C. Argyris, "Human Problems With Budgets," *Harvard Business Review*, January–February, 1953, pp. 97–110.

[7] Dr. V. N. Morris, *The Basic Philosophy behind a Separate Budget for Research and Development*, Proceedings of the Fifth Annual Conference on the Administration of Research. New York: Columbia University Press, 1954, p. 189. See also George W. Howard, *Common Sense in Research and Development Management*. New York: Vintage Books, Inc., 1955, p. 56.

[8] Dr. Vannevar Bush, *op. cit.*, p. 10. See also Howard K. Nason, *Problems in Programming and Scheduling*, Special Report No. 6. New York: American Management Association, 1955, pp. 95–97.

[9] Jules D. Porsche, *Ibid.*, p. 38.

[10] H. J. Finison, *Control of Cost of Research and Development Projects*, Proceedings of the National Electronic Conference, Vol. 9. Chicago: Illinois Institute of Technology, 1954, p. 854.

through company-sponsored programs or university courses. One of the three companies studied sponsored a training program for supervisory personnel to which project leaders were invited. Management should encourage and provide a means for project leaders and engineers to gain administrative ability by sponsoring management-training courses and/or by offering financial assistance and time off for individual study. To date, both management and scientific personnel have placed more emphasis on scientific knowledge to help in coordinating and leading laboratory personnel. But there is a dire need for administrative know-how, and the project leader must balance his efforts to acquire both technical and administrative training.

Training programs are long-range measures for alleviating the problem, but more immediate measures are also necessary. In my opinion, the project leader should adopt the project-budgetary scheme described and recommended in this chapter. Management should encourage and help project leaders to learn its usefulness by providing the time and services of its accounting personnel. In addition to this, management should set up streamlined training courses in areas like human relations and planning as temporary measures to help project leaders gain the skills necessary and to gain time to establish longer-range programs.

With the need for industrial R & D growing and competition for technologically qualified scientists becoming progressively acute, the lack of administrative training on the part of project leaders specifically gains in importance. Because of low predictability, scientists and engineers feel that more stress on technological ability is the best approach. I concede that it is a meaningful approach, but I argue that by itself it is not enough. More administrative training and the use of adaptations of tailor-made planning devices should do much to augment the output of the laboratory. Overemphasis on more technology at the risk of proper administrative ability, in the face of growing competition and growing amounts of financial investments in R & D, would generate chaos.

In its early history budgeting was criticized as being extremely inaccurate and time consuming, a devious management device, and inconsistent with a good working climate and the general realities of changing business conditions. However, history has more recently shown that effective planning, with much help of the progressively refined budgetary device, has become the main theme and way of life in the financial, marketing, and manufacturing phases of business and industry.

In my opinion, budgeting will develop and find more use in industrial research and development, and with more emphasis on the use of administrative processes at the project level, the project leader will become more effective in the budgetary process.

Bibliography

ANDERSON, DAVID R., *Practical Controllership*. Homewood, Ill.: Richard D. Irwin, Inc., 1951.
ANTHONY, ROBERT N., *Management Controls in Industrial Research Organizations*. Cambridge, Mass.: Harvard University Press, 1952.
ARGYRIS, C., "Human Problems with Budgets," *Harvard Business Review*, 1953.
BUSH, VANNEVAR, *Science and Business*. An address, Rutgers University, 1958.
CONANT, JAMES B., *On Understanding Science*. New Haven, Conn.: Yale University Press, 1947.
DALE, ERNEST, *Planning and Developing the Company Organization Structure*, Research Report No. 20. New York: American Management Association, 1957.
DEAN, JOEL, *Capital Budgeting*, 3d ed. Englewood Cliffs, N. J.: Prentice-Hall, Inc., 1956.
FINISON, H. J., *Control of Cost of Research and Development Projects*, Proceedings of the National Electronic Conference, vol. 9. Chicago: Illinois Institute of Technology, 1954.
GROVENSTEIN, ERLING, JR., "Some Factors in the Choice of Basic Research Problems in Science," *The Research Engineer*, July, 1956.
HOWARD, GEORGE W., *Common Sense in Research and Development Management*. New York: Vintage Books, Inc., 1955.
MCGRAW-HILL DEPARTMENT OF ECONOMICS, *Business' Plans for New Plants and Equipment 1962/1965*, 15th Annual Survey. New York: McGraw-Hill Publishing Company, Inc., 1962.
MERRILL, LYNCH, PIERCE, FENNER & SMITH, *R & D and the Investor*. New York: Merrill, Lynch, Pierce, Fenner & Smith, Inc., 1960.
MORRIS, V. N., *The Basic Philosophy behind a Separate Budget for Research and Development*, Proceedings of the Fifth Annual Conference on the Administration of Research. New York: Columbia University Press, 1954.

NASON, HOWARD K., *Problems in Programming and Scheduling*, Special Report No. 6. New York: American Management Association, 1955.

NATIONAL SCIENCE FOUNDATION, *Federal Funds for Science X* (NSF 61-82). Washington, D. C.: Government Printing Office, 1962.

————, *Funds for Research and Development in Industry* (NSF 62-3). Washington, D. C.: Government Printing Office, 1959.

NICKERSON, CLARENCE B., *Cost Accounting*. New York: McGraw-Hill Book Company, Inc., 1954.

PORSCHE, JULES D., *Creative Ability: Its Role in the Search for New Products*, Special Report No. 6. New York: American Management Association, 1955.

QUINN, JAMES B., "How Industry Uses R & D Budgets," *The Management Review*, 1959.

SALZBERG, PAUL L., "Progress through Coordinated Effort," *Getting the Most from Product Research and Development*, Special Report No. 6. New York: American Management Association, 1955.

SAMUELSON, PAUL A., *Economics*, 4th ed. New York: McGraw-Hill Book Company, Inc., 1955.

SCHUMPETER, J. A., "The Stability of Capitalism," *Economic Journal*, September 1928.

WHITING, CHARLES S., *Creative Thinking*. New York: Reinhold Publishing Corporation, 1958.

Index

Accomplishment, motivation (*see* Motivation)
   project personnel, 25, 76
   project technical, 46
Accounting department, 29, 44, 45
Administration, budgeting (*see* Budgeting)
   of changes, 36, 37
   project leader (*see* Project leader)
   R & D (*see* Research and development)
Administrative process, 2
Aircraft and parts industry, 2
Allocations, of funds (*see* Funds)
   laboratory costs, 42
   project costs, 41
   remaining resources for project, 53
Anderson, David R., 139
Appropriations, (*see* Funds)
Approval of "process," 36, 37
   annual laboratory budget, 42
   individual project budget, 43, 51
Argyris, C., 139
Arnold, John E., creativity, 70, 71
Assignment of work, 59, 62, 75
   alternatives, consideration of, 108
   chief engineer (*see* Chief engineer)
   line engineer (*see* Line engineer)
   management (*see* Management)
   project leader (*see* Project leader)
Assignment of work (*Cont.*)
   project progress review (*see* Project progress review)
   scheduling, 80
   subproject breakdown, effect on, 84
   vague specifications, effects of, 74, 79
Authority, organizational, of project

Authority (*Cont.*)
   leader over line engineer, 56, 59, 60, 89
   see also Assignment of work

"Blue sky," 62, 98
"Brain quality," 25
Breakthrough, 17
Budget, annual laboratory, 36, 38, 39, 40
   capital, 36, 40
   organizational requirements, 26, 27
   project, 28, 29, 30
   scheduling, 27, 29
   uses of: annual laboratory budget, 28, 30, 42, 43
      project budget, 29, 30, 40–43
      by project leader, 33
   see also Budgetary process, standard
Budgetary process, cutoff decisions, 31
   decisions, approval of, 5, 37
   planning tool, 72
   project selection, 32
   standard, 36
      annual laboratory budget, 36, 38, 39, 72: approval, 42; capital, 36; formulation, 41
      changes, administration of: frequency of revision, 48; laboratory budget, 48, 49; project budget, 48, 49, 53, 54
      checking up on progress: project resources, adequacy of remaining, 53; laboratory budget, 43–49; project budget, 43–47
      definition of, 36
      development of, 36

145

Budgetary process (*Cont.*)
    expense budget, 36
    monthly progress reviews, 43
    project budget, 36, 37, 39: approval, 43, 51; formulation, 40, 50
    overhead allocation, 36
    preparation period, 49
    project leader, role of (*see* Project leader)
    responsibilities, 37
    see also Budgeting
Budgeting, definition of, 3
    engineers, number of, 24
    expenditures, checking up on, 30
    in manufacturing, 3
    management, 28 (*see also* Management, budgeting)
    planning device, 8
    ratios, 29
    subject matter of, 8
    for subprojects, 104, 105
    usefulness of, 6
    working climate, 93
    see also Predictability; Project leader
"Bumping," 80
Bush, Vannevar, 138, 140

Capital, budgets for laboratory, 36, 40
    demand for, 2
    expenditures, 32
Cash flow, 28, 30, 41
Changes, administration of, 34, 36, 37, 48, 49, 53, 54
    by chief engineer, 48, 49, 53, 54
    by division manager, 48, 49
    laboratory budget, causes, 48
    project budget, causes, 48
    by project leader, 48, 53, 54
    revision, frequency of, 48
    sources of, 49
    timetable, effect on, 84
    vague specifications, effects of, 74, 79
Checking-up, on expenditures, 30
    on over-all progress, 43, 44
    project progress review (*see* Project progress review)
    on technical progress, 28
    variance analysis, 44–46
Chemical industry, expenditures in, 2
Chemistry, 4, 11
Chief engineer, 5, 26
    budget preparation, 49
    budget, uses of, 28–40

Chief engineer, budget (*Cont.*)
    limitations facing project leader, 55, 57, 61, 62
    changes, administration of, 53, 54
    cutoff, 76
    job description, 13
    laboratory budget, approval of, 42
    monthly progress review, 44, 46, 47
    performance, 82–84
    project budget, approval of, 43
    responsibilities in budgetary process, 37, 40
    selection of experiments, 52, 53
"Chinese copy," 9, 14
"Combining" knowledge, 15
Communication, budgeting, effect on, 66
    in organization, 88–92
    among project personnel, 63, 65, 75, 76
    working climate, 93
Communication device, definition of, 95
    faulty information, 96, 97
    understanding among disciplines, effects of, 97
Communication process, 91, 92
Communications industry, expenditures in, 2
Competition for engineer's time, 60, 78
Competition, market, 43, 49, 84
Competitor, market, 56
Completion date, specification change, effects of, 84
    vague specifications, effects of, 74, 79
    target-type, 82
    timetable (*see* Timetable)
Conant, James B., 138
"Contingency" sum, 48
Control, budget (*see* Budget)
    management, 25
    of R & D costs, 3, 29
Coordination, 62
    management (*see* Management)
    predictability, 94
    project leader, 90 (*see also* Project leader, coordination)
Cost, labor, 14, 39, 40
    laboratory and project budget, monitoring, 30
    material, 39, 40
    variance, 44, 46, 47
Cost control (*see* Control)
"Crash," a sample project, 14, 15, 17

Crash program, 15, 61, 80
Creative process, 71, 75, 79, 93
Creativity, definition of, 127
    line engineer, 70
    planning, balances against, 128
Cutoff of experiments, 28, 31, 60, 63, 64, 65, 73, 108
    budgeting, effects on, 63
    considerations, general, 76, 77
    untimely, 76, 77

Data, historical accounting, 29
    estimating project budget, 40, 41
Dean, Joel, 2
Decisions, alternative considerations, 101, 102
    economics of, 101
    making of, 89, 90, 101
Discovery, cutoff, 77
    see also Innovation; Probability of success
Division manager (*see* Manager)
"Doubled in Brass," project leader, 12
Dovetailing, 5, 27, 59, 60, 79, 84

Economic considerations, 101, 102
Education, 129, 130
    courses, scope and cost of, 129
    programs, alternative, 122
    for project leader, 78
    see also Recommendations to management
Educational institutions, 1
Engineer, assignment to projects, 5, 34
    chief engineer (*see* Chief engineer)
    individual output, 25
    laboratory, number for, 24
    line engineer (*see* Line engineer)
    national shortage, 84, 93, 131
    project leader, 12 (*see also* Project leader)
Engineering, development and design, 3, 5
    electrical, 4, 11
    labor cost, 14, 39, 40
    man-hours (*see* Man-hours)
    project, 5
    semiconductor development, 5, 14–16, 17–22
Engineering services, 11
Equipment, 40
    see also Capital, budgets

Error, 71, 75
    margin of, 41, 50, 58, 59
Estimates, accuracy of, 62
    faulty, 44, 46, 52
    man-hours (*see* Man-hours)
    by project leader, 58, 59
    project progress review, 44–47
Expenditures, R & D, capital equipment, 14, 32
    federal government, 1
    private industry, 1
    R & D laboratory, 32
Expenses, control, laboratory and project budget, 29, 30
    definition of, 37–39
Experience, cutoff, 77
    of line engineer, 68
    of project leader, 68
    of technical personnel, 58
Experiment, 34, 52, 59, 74
    continuation of, 63, 77, 87, 97
    coordination of, 80
    criterion of selection, 33, 52
    cutoff decision making, 76, 77 (*see also* Cutoff of experiments)
    definition of, 15
    design of, 56, 79
    methods, 68
    "runs," 56, 74
    solutions to, 15, 58, 62
    success, probability of (*see* Probability of success)
    trial and error, method, 74

Finison, H. J., 140
Firm, appraisal of, 2
    reputation and prestige of, 42
Flow (*see* Information)
Forecasting, budget process, 68, 75
    experiments, runs or cycles of, 58
    information, by guesses, 68
    predictability (*see* Predictability)
    in production vs. in R & D, 69
    project budget, 58
    technical problems, 58
    transfer of experience (MTM), 70
Formulation of budgetary process, 36, 37
    laboratory budget, annual, 41
    project budget, 40, 50
Formulation system for project budget, 105
Frustration (*see* Human relations)

Functional group heads, 59, 60
  job description, 11, 13
Funds, adequacy of remaining, 116
  chief engineer performance affected by, 83
  for laboratory, 47
  for project, 64, 83, 110, 116
  project progress review (*see* Project progress review, funds)
  allocation of, 24
  alternative-choice decisions, 116
  appropriations for R & D, 3, 5, 28, 29, 30
  faulty laboratory and project allocation, 43–47
  insufficient, 27
  usage rate, 24

Germanium, 8
Government, federal, expenditures, 1
Growth, 1, 2
"Guesses," 68, 70
  see also Information; Predictability

Hiring, 26, 93
Human relations, communication process, 92
  competition for line engineer, 78
  curiosity, 77
  cutoff, 77
  frustration, 77
  handling people, 74, 77
  interaction of personnel, 120
  organizational requirements, 93, 94
  progress, 92
  project leader authority, 91
  project personnel selection, 92
  project selection, 93
  understanding other disciplines, 60, 92
  unity of command, 91
  working climate, 92, 93
  see also Chief engineer; Line engineer; Project leader

Ideas for new project, 9
Incentive, project personnel, 94
  see also Motivation
Industry, private, 1
Information, 35
  definition of, 91
  flow, 65, 69, 73, 88
  forecasting, 68
  in R & D, 75

Information (*Cont.*)
  sources of, 68
  see also Communication; Guesses; Planning
Innovation, 2
Instruments industry, expenditures in, 2
Investments, 2, 28, 32, 42
  see also Dean, Joel; Samuelson, Paul A.

Know-how, interdisciplinary, 4, 10, 12, 59, 88
  lack of, in project leader, 60, 97
  line engineer, in budgeting, 63, 139
  project leader, in administration and budgeting, 64, 78, 86, 101, 139

Laboratory, administration of changes, 39, 48
  allocation of funds for, 24
  annual budget, 36–38, 41, 42
  budget preparation period, 40
  budget, uses of, 28, 29, 30
  capital budget (*see* Capital budget)
  expenditures, 32
  facilities, 14
  progress review, 43–47
  size of, 24
  standard annual budget, 28, 29, 41–43
  structure, 10–12, 89
  see also Capital budget; Organization
Laboratory organizational units, functional, 10, 11
  size of, 39
Line engineer, 10, 13, 33, 34
  assignment of work to, 60, 62, 93
  creativity (*see* Creativity, line engineer)
  definition of, 13
  drawbacks to interchangeability, 60, 61, 82
  faulty information, sources of, 73, 97
  human relations, 77
  job description, 13
  motivation (*see* Motivation)
  organizational requirements, 93, 94
  performance of, 76
  programming project work, 33
    project leader performance, effects on, 91
  scheduling of time, 79, 80

Index

Line Engineer (*Cont.*)
  supervision of, 59
  understanding of other sciences, 60, 92, 97

Machinery industry, electrical, 2
Management, 6
  budgeting, 28 (*see also* Budgeting, management)
  budgets, approval, 41, 42, 43
  coordination, 27
  cutoff, 31
  decisions in R & D administration and control, 7, 23, 25–28
  project changes, 34
  project progress review, 43–47
  responsibility to budgetary process, 37, 40, 41
  top, 5, 6, 37
  unity of command, 91
  see also Chief engineer; Functional group heads; Research and development; Project leader
Manager, of division, 11, 37, 42
  administering changes, 48, 49
  approval of budgets, 43
    monthly project progress review, 43–47
  manufacturing, 30
Man-hours, 40, 41
  budget process (*see* Project, budget)
  estimation of, 68
  translation (*see* Translation, man-hours to timetable and dollars)
Manpower, allocation of, 5, 24
  control on laboratory budget, 83
  planning for, 24
  scheduling, effects of, 84
Manufacturing, 2, 3, 5, 10, 11
  see also Production
Market, 33, 41, 84, 85, 86
Material, cost, 39, 40
  requirement, 59, 62
McGraw-Hill series on R & D expenditures, 2
Mechanical engineering, 4, 11
Meeting, informal, 33, 47
  see also Project progress review
"Mental dexterity," 85
Metallurgy, 4, 11
Model shop, 25
  see also Services
Morale, 5
  see also Human relations

Motivation, 60, 63, 66, 76, 77, 97

Nason, Howard K., 140
National economic growth, 1
National Science Foundation, 1

Operating-cost report, 45, 46
Organization, communication, 88–94
  functional units, 10, 11
  laboratory structure, 5, 10, 11
  size of, 24
  typical R & D laboratory, 10, 11, 89
  see also Authority, organizational
Organization and communication, 88–94
  implications, 92–94
  limitations to working climate, 93
  project leader responsibility to project, 88
Organizational encumbrances, 89, 91
Organizational requirements, 26, 94
Overhead, 36, 39, 40
Overtime, 27, 44

Parameters (*see* Production; Research and development)
Patents, 25
Performance, 25, 75
  financial, 28
  measurement, 3
  over-all project, 51
  of project team, 41
  project technical, 28
  see also Chief engineer; Line engineer; Project leader
Personnel management, authority over line engineers, 56, 59, 60 (*see also* Authority, organizational)
  see also Engineer; Human relations; Recommendations to management
Petroleum industry, expenditures in, 2
Physics, 4, 11
Planning, 6, 56
  budget (*see* Budget)
  comprehensive approach, 138
  definition of, 72
  effect on budgeting, 62
  effective, 73, 76, 93, 125, 140
  faulty, 62
  good, 69, 77
  ineffective, 74–78
  information, 68, 69
  meaningful, 61, 62
  nondollar device, 106

Planning (Cont.)
  optimum timing for, 125
  process for production, 68, 69
  R & D, 68–70
  by project leader, 58
  versus creativity, 127, 128
  see also Chief engineer; Line engineer; Programming; Project leader
Planning and scheduling, effects, 84
  faulty communications, 98, 99
  implications to budgeting and project leader, 82–87, 100
  low predictability, 72
  short vs. long projects, 86
  see also Project leader
Porsche, Jules D., 139, 140
Predictability, 17, 68, 73
  in budgeting, 58, 59, 68–70
  increase of, 67
  low, 58, 59, 67, 73, 75, 76, 84
    arresting of, 80
    budgeting, effects on, 59
    manpower, effects on, 84
    human relations, 92
    scheduling device (see Scheduling device)
    significance of, 69
  and uncertainty, 67
Pressure, 93, 138, 139
  see also Human relations
Priority, criteria for, 100
  ranking of projects, 51
Probability of success, 15, 16, 17, 31, 52, 58, 63, 76
Problems (see Technical problems)
"Process," 36, 37
  see also Project progress review; Standard budgetary process
Processes, new, 2
Product, 2, 4, 32
Production, 3, 4, 69–71
Productivity, 2, 3, 25, 70
Professional societies, 25
Profit, 2, 3, 28, 32
Profit and loss statement, 28, 32
Programming, 15, 73, 80, 84
  nondollar planning, 106
  project budget, proposed system for, 105
  regular, 15
  see also Planning
Progress review, total laboratory, 43, 47

Project, average length of time, 14
  budget, 28, 29, 30, 41, 55–66, 105
    standard, 36, 37, 39, 41–49
    changes, 34
  ideas for, 9
  in-process, 68
  multidisciplinary, 14, 62
  profitability, new products, 32
  sample, 14
  selection of, 5, 9, 27, 32, 40
  short vs. long, 86
  size of, 41
  solution, methods of, 68
  success, 15
  technical proposal, 16
  technical specifications, 33
  timetable, 5, 99
  usage and allocation of funds, 24, 41
Project leader, 5, 6, 10, 26, 33
  administering changes, 53, 54
  assignment of, 12
  authority, effect on, budgeting, 60
    over line engineers, 59, 60, 89
    scheduling, 80, 82
  budget, use of, 33, 34, 98–102
  budgeting, 6, 8, 49
  coordination and planning, 58, 59, 62, 73–79, 88, 89, 90, 98, 102
  cutoff, 76, 77
  definition of, 12
  effects on chief engineer performance, 82–84
  encumbrances to coordinating, 89–91
  forecasting, 68
  forecasting process, 68
  handling of people, 73, 74, 77
  job description, 12, 91
  limitations in budgetary process, 55–60
  performance, 54, 91
  recruiting, 131
  responsibilities, of, 5, 88, 90
  role in administration, 33, 34, 48, 88
  role in standard budgetary process, 37, 49–54
  scheduling difficulties, 79
  understanding of other sciences, 60, 92, 97
  work load, 78
  working climate, 25
Project progress review, characteristics of, 96
  communication, 91, 92, 95
  corrective action, 34, 44–47, 65

Project progress review (*Cont.*)
  daily work assignments, 96, 98, 100
  faulty, 65, 98
  information, faulty, 73, 96
  over-all project, 43–47
  process of, 64
  project budget, 43
  provision for changes, 49
  purpose of, 47, 95, 96
  recommended system, 107
  remaining funds, 100
  timetable, 99
  understanding, faulty, 60, 73, 92, 97
  variance analysis, 44–47
Project team, 10–12, 93, 94

Ratios, 29, 30, 41
Recommendations for budgetary process, 111, 112
  benefits of, 110
  broader progress reviews, 104
  changes to scheduling system, 108
  justification of, 113
  requirements for, 111
  subproject budgeting, 104
  variance analysis procedure, 104
Recommendations to management, 123, 125, 128–131
Recommendations to project leader, 117–123
Recovery time, definition of, 85, 86
Recruiting, 131
Research, pure, applied, 4, 5
Research and development (R & D), administration, 2, 5, 6, 7, 23, 28–31, 141
  appropriation of funds, 3, 28
  costs, control of, 3, 29
  economics of, 2
  in electronics, 4
  expenditures, 1, 30
  function, 6–8
  industrial, 2, 3
  input-output parameters, 69–71, 75
  objective of, 3
  output, evaluation of, 3
  performance measurement, 3
  planning, 3, 68–70
  in semiconductor field, 4
  work, 10, 13, 14, 25–28, 68–71
  see also Budgeting; Innovation; Investments; Organization; Uncertainty

Resources, definition of, 127
  for project, 99–102, 127

Sales, 5, 10, 11, 28
Sales department, 29
Samuelson, Paul A., 2
Scheduling, 15, 27
  advantages of, 79–80
  disadvantages to, 79, 80
  dovetailing, 84
  laboratory work load, 85, 86
  of line engineers' time, 81
  minimizing spread of manpower, 84, 85
  simultaneous vs. tandem, 85, 86
  see also Scheduling device
Scheduling device, 56, 39
  budgeting, effects on, 59
  difficulties of, 79–82
  low predictability, 79
  for project leader, 78–82
  vague specifications, effects of, 74, 79
  see also Scheduling
Scheduling systems, 109
Schumpeter, J. A., 2
Science, 1
Scientists, assignment of, 5
Selection, of problem definitions, 58
  of project team, 93
  see also Experiment; Project, selection of
Semiconductor, 4, 5
Service groups, 39
Services, 14, 35, 59, 62, 68, 80, 99, 121
Silicon, 8
Solutions, experiment, methods of, 68
Specifications, 58
  dummy, 125
  vague, 56–58, 73, 74, 79
Standard of living, 1
Stanford University, 70
Stretch-out," definition of, 43
Subproblem, 62, 83, 84
Subproject, 15, 75, 104
Summary of findings, 133, 135, 136, 137
Switching, 60, 85

Teamwork, 34, 93
Technical experiments, 33
Technical feasibility, 33, 68
Technical mileposts, 46
Technical objectives, 15, 33

Index

Technical problems, 15, 16, 40, 58, 68, 75 (*see also* Probability of success)
Technical progress, 28, 44, 51, 52
Technical proposal, project, 15, 16, 40, 62, 73, 75
Technical solutions, 16, 40
Technical specifications (*see* Specifications)
Technology, 2
Time, budget and progress, effect on, 83
  length of project, average, 14
  line engineer, distribution of, 81
  short vs. long project, 86
Timetable, 84, 99 (*see also* Completion date)
Training, 121, 122, 129, 130, 140
Transistor, 8, 9
  type X, 14, 15, 17
  uses, 9
Translation, 68

Uncertainty, 6, 15, 58, 59, 75
  effects on subproblem breakdown, 84
  forecasting budget process, 67
  production vs. R & D, 69, 70
  in R & D, 68, 69

Uncertainty (*Cont.*)
  short vs. long project, 86
  see also Predictability
Unity of command, 91

Variance analysis, 44, 46, 107
Variance report, 44

Work assignment (*see* Assignment of work)
Working climate, 25
  effect of predictability, 94
  sources of pressure in, 93
Work load, 56, 59
  chief engineer, 61
  functional groups, 39
  line engineers, 59, 60, 85
  loading laboratory, 85, 86
  number of projects per line engineer, 60
  planning ahead, 64, 96, 98
  project leader, 78
  vague specifications, effects of, 79
  see also Assignment of work; Scheduling
Work projection, 98, 99 (*see also* Project progress review; Services)

T
175.5
m64